P 1

F

MW00615522

GUEST EDITOR
Andrea Barrett

DEPARTING EDITOR
Don Lee

MANAGING EDITOR
Robert Arnold

DEPARTING POETRY EDITOR
David Daniel

ASSOCIATE FICTION EDITOR
Maryanne O'Hara

INTERIM EXECUTIVE DIRECTOR
DeWitt Henry

FOUNDING PUBLISHER
Peter O'Malley

ADVISORY EDITORS

Sherman Alexie
Russell Banks
Charles Baxter
Ann Beattie
Madison Smartt Bell
Anne Bernays
Frank Bidart
Amy Bloom
Robert Boswell
Henry Bromell
Rosellen Brown
Ron Carlson
James Carroll
Madeline DeFrees
Mark Doty
Rita Dove
Stuart Dybek
Cornelius Eady
Martín Espada
Carolyn Forché
Richard Ford
George Garrett
Lorrie Goldensohn
Mary Gordon
Jorie Graham
David Gullette
Marilyn Hacker
Donald Hall

Joy Harjo
Stratis Haviaras
DeWitt Henry
Edward Hirsch
Jane Hirshfield
Alice Hoffman
Fanny Howe
Marie Howe
Gish Jen
Justin Kaplan
Bill Knott
Yusef Komunyakaa
Maxine Kumin
Philip Levine
Margot Livesey
Thomas Lux
Gail Mazur
Campbell McGrath
Heather McHugh
James Alan McPherson
Sue Miller
Lorrie Moore
Paul Muldoon
Antonya Nelson
Jay Neugeboren
Howard Norman
Tim O'Brien
Joyce Peseroff

Carl Phillips
Jayne Anne Phillips
Robert Pinsky
Alberto Ríos
Lloyd Schwartz
Jane Shore
Charles Simic
Gary Soto
Elizabeth Spires
David St. John
Maura Stanton
Gerald Stern
Mark Strand
Christopher Tilghman
Richard Tillinghast
Chase Twichell
Fred Viebahn
Ellen Bryant Voigt
Dan Wakefield
Derek Walcott
Rosanna Warren
Alan Williamson
Tobias Wolff
C. D. Wright
Al Young
Kevin Young

PLOUGHSHARES, a journal of new writing, is guest-edited serially by prominent writers who explore different and personal visions, aesthetics, and literary circles. PLOUGHSHARES is published in April, August, and December at Emerson College, 120 Boylston Street, Boston, MA 02116-4624. Telephone: (617) 824-8753. Web address: pshares.org.

EDITORIAL ASSISTANTS: Kat Setzer and Blair Hurley. BOOKSHELF ADVISORS: Fred Leebron and Cate Marvin. ASSISTANT FICTION EDITOR: Jay Baron Nicorvo. PROOFREADER: Megan Weireter.

FICTION READERS: Laura van den Berg, Simeon Berry, Kathleen Rooney, Kat Setzer, Chip Cheek, Jim Scott, Cam Terwilliger, Steve Himmer, August Hohenstein, Sara Whittleton, Vanessa Carlisle, Chris Helmuth, Eson Kim, Wendy Wunder, Brenda Pike, Leslie Busler, Dan Medeiros, James Charlesworth, Emily Ekle, Patricia Reed, Gregg Rosenblum, Hannah Bottomy, Shannon Derby, and Jason Roeder. POETRY READERS: Simeon Berry, Kathleen Rooney, Autumn McClintock, Heather Madden, Elisa Gabbert, Julia Story, Jennifer Kohl, Pepe Abola, Chris Tonelli, Maria Halovanic, David Semanki, Zachary Sifuentes, and Meredith Devney.

SUBSCRIPTIONS (ISSN 0048-4474): $24 for one year (3 issues), $46 for two years (6 issues); $27 a year for institutions. Add $12 a year for international ($10 for Canada).

UPCOMING: Winter 2007–08, a poetry and fiction issue edited by Philip Levine, will appear in December 2007. Spring 2008, a poetry and fiction issue edited by B. H. Fairchild, will appear in April 2008.

SUBMISSIONS: Reading period is from August 1 to March 31 (postmark and online dates). All submissions sent from April to July are returned unread. Please see page 221 for editorial and submission policies.

Back-issue, classroom-adoption, and bulk orders may be placed directly through PLOUGHSHARES. Microfilms of back issues may be obtained from University Microfilms. PLOUGHSHARES is also available as CD-ROM and full-text products from EBSCO, H.W. Wilson, ProQuest, and the Gale Group. Indexed in M.L.A. Bibliography, American Humanities Index, Index of American Periodical Verse, Book Review Index. Full publisher's index is online at pshares.org. The views and opinions expressed in this journal are solely those of the authors. All rights for individual works revert to the authors upon publication. PLOUGHSHARES receives support from the National Endowment for the Arts and the Massachusetts Cultural Council.

Retail distribution by Ingram Periodicals. Printed in the U.S.A. by Edwards Brothers.

© 2007 by Emerson College   ISBN 1-933058-07-2

CONTENTS

Fall 2007

Cover art:
Specimens of Gray by Lisa Nilsson
Mixed media assemblage, 12″ x 12″, 2005

Ploughshares Patrons

This nonprofit publication would not be possible without the
support of our readers and the generosity of the following
individuals and organizations.

COUNCIL
William H. Berman
Denise and Mel Cohen
Robert E. Courtemanche
Jacqueline Liebergott
Fannette H. Sawyer Fund
Turow Foundation
Eugenia Gladstone Vogel
Marillyn Zacharis

PATRONS
Audrey Taylor Gonzalez
Drs. Jay and Mary Anne Jackson
Alice Munro
Joanne Randall, in memory of
James Randall

FRIENDS
Jorie Hofstra
Tom Jenks and Carol Edgarian

ORGANIZATIONS
Bank of America Foundation
Emerson College
Houghton Mifflin
Massachusetts Cultural Council
National Endowment for the Arts

COUNCIL: $3,000 for two lifetime subscriptions and
acknowledgement in the journal for three years.
PATRON: $1,000 for a lifetime subscription and
acknowledgement in the journal for two years.
FRIEND: $500 for a lifetime subscription and
acknowledgement in the journal for one year.

Introduction

In Ovid's *Metamorphoses,* a boy turns into a daffodil, a girl turns into a tree, a husband and wife turn into snakes and slither away together. The fisherman Glaucus, seeing the fish he's just caught return to life after he's spread them out on the meadow, eats one of the strange leaves they're lying on and turns into a green-bearded, blue-armed sea god. What happens in what we call real life is no less strange. I like it when such moments of transformation, utterly strange, utterly essential, find their way into fiction.

Transformation has been on my mind a lot, partly because I've been immersed in Darwin's work these past two years and partly because during that time I've been living in an old brick mill building in North Adams, Massachusetts. During the summer of 1911, photographer Lewis Hine documented some of the children who worked here, turning cotton into cloth. (In one photo, a dozen young boys have been herded together in front of the building; the littlest boy, barefoot, is happily smoking a pipe.) Other things were made in this building later, after the textile industry collapsed. Now, shiitake mushrooms grow in what was once the weave shed across the street, while art grows here. Found family snapshots, lost for decades, turn into videos accompanying new music compositions. Sheets of Plexiglas turn into transparent buildings, clay is shaped into haunting figures, old bones and dead ants combine into new arrangements. A green garden hose turns into a cactus, and words turn into poems and stories. Pigments and scraps of text and marble dust and fibers turn into paintings large or small, abstract or figurative, while soldiers' faces and stories are captured in piercing photographs. When longtime North Adams residents, intrigued by the building's evolution, come by to visit, they tell stories about working here in earlier days. As a teenager, one neighbor said, he sewed together the components of canvas postal bags for a company that occupied one floor of the building. Later, assembling sleeping bags, he worked in a vast room filled with floating white down.

It's hard, in this environment, *not* to think about the transformations of people, places, and relationships over time, or about how things designed for one purpose can be used, so interestingly, for another. Lisa Nilsson's *Specimens of Gray,* an image of which graces this issue's cover, playfully embodies some of these ideas. A box 12″ x 12″ in the original, it's described by the artist as an "assemblage composed of found and made objects placed in niches carved into a plywood support and then sealed under glass. Mixed media including: balloon-end, gouache rendering of balloon-end, balloon-end crewel worked in thread, scrimshaw of plastic monkey head, plaster cast of plastic monkey head, mouse molar, typewriting, and topographic paper sculptures."

The mouse molar is the same as it ever was, but also—freshly visible in all its beauty and singularity—not the same. The best fiction performs the same miracle, selecting from all that is around us, every minute, those words and images that make us *pay attention.* Editing this issue of *Ploughshares,* reading so many complex and resonant stories, I chose those in which precise language restores what we otherwise, out of habit, fail to notice. Those that capture the mystery of metamorphosis; those in which characters are transformed by love, rage, grief, exile, politics, religion, art. In the stories gathered here, characters change, often despite their own resistance. Their understanding of their earlier lives changes, as the world—constantly, obdurately present—changes around them. Guns go off, alewives glitter like mirrors, venomous serpents flick their tongues and offer salvation or death. Families add members, lose members, transpose their relationships—and all the time the rest of the world is also, always, in flux. I love stories that, fusing the inner life and the outer life, register the transformations in both. I hope you will enjoy these stories, too.

KAREN E. BENDER

Reunion

When Anna Green walked into the ballroom for the twentieth reunion of Surfview High in Los Angeles, she did not predict that she would fall in love with Warren Vance. She joined her classmates, in their finery, penned by the hotel's large glass windows, the sky outside black and the cars on the freeways arranged in a parade of pure light. She walked in alone, as her husband had not wanted to come, and it was startling to walk into this festive room by herself, almost shocking, as though her world at home had been imagined.

Anna walked past Johnny the Weatherman, who was describing the weather across the world. Johnny used to run around the high school clutching maps and telling people detailed weather reports—he received thunderous applause at graduation, as though people were paying tribute that they were not him, or that they had been generally kind to him. He was now almost forty, older, angrier, but still standing in front of the crowd with the same map. "There is snow in Denmark and a drought in the Midwest, and fires raging across Mexico," he said, gesturing to a map with a pointer. No one appeared to be listening; the room roared.

She listened to her classmates describe their lives, which all sounded strangely the same. There were the free agents, the childless, the ones living abroad, the briefly famous—there were those who were unaccounted for, there were those who were already dead—but most were, at this point in the continuum, employed and organized into the strict nations of family. There was Tiara Hanson, the popular girl who loved reunions because she was in her glory for four hours once every ten years. Her hair was abundant, her teeth perfect and unmarked. "Anna!" she said, placing her hand on Anna's shoulder. "You look fifteen! Don't we all." Tiara indulged in the same self-congratulation that seduced their classmates twenty years ago. There was Stuart McKenzie, who had been an avid collector of baseball cards and now served as a statistician for the achievements of his children, holding out photos of them engaged in myriad activities: "Benny was first clarinet in his school orchestra," he said. The children stared, imprisoned by their father's desire to have something to love; they peered out, wanting to run across streets, to drive cars.

Anna hugged, shook hands, and introduced herself over and over: she had been married eight years to Howard Fine, had two children, Dan, six, and Sophie, two, worked at a business repairing washers and dryers all over the Southland; customers saw her at the door, a woman technician, and often asked to see her ID. She liked walking into the homes of strangers to fix their washers, dryers, refrigerators, their Kenwoods, Maytags, Frigidaires—she also liked to see their wallpaper, the arrangement of their furniture, the optimistic attempts to claim their right to the world.

She was not looking for Warren Vance, whom she had loved first, before all this. He had been a skinny, swaggering boy with an overconfidence that was thrilling then, as though every adult's failure was a conscious and unfortunate decision. He was going to be a congressman, a TV news producer, a real estate tycoon. Sometimes she caught him muttering the inaugural address in his sleep. He wet his hair with his palms in the morning and brushed it so it looked like Donald Trump's. He had been obsessed with table manners, hostess presents, anything that he believed would help him ascend. His father had died when he was two, and his mother was remote and frustrated; he had a frantic quality to him, as though waiting for someone to tell him to stop. He asked her to marry him with a large trophy, a small metal man running at the top. At the bottom there was a plaque that read: "Congratulations! You are awarded a golden future with Mr. Warren R. Vance."

She had met Warren in high-school auto shop. Johnny the Weatherman had been standing by a car parked under a blue sky. "A storm front is moving in from the Pacific," he announced, panicked. "We have to get this inside. Anna Green's the fastest. Anna Green should fix it."

She was the best in auto shop and a little uncomfortable about this, but also proud. She stepped in front of all the boys and put her hands into the engine. Warren was casing the class, looking for who would help him pass it. He was lanky, prone to hostile jokes, and had trouble standing in one place. But while she fixed the engine, she could sense him pausing, absorbing what she was doing, and when she glanced up at him, his face twitched; it was the one time she saw he was afraid.

The first time he touched her face, it was as though he were cradling a piece of crystal in his palms. She had been drawn in by Warren's certainty, the contrived certainty of the abandoned; he had believed that she was the most desirable girl on earth, and this certainty was alien and gratifying. He was prone to general suspicion toward those who did not admire him, and he left when she did not agree to marry him at twenty. "No one will love you the way Vance will," he said, and vanished. It took her years before she stopped believing she saw him on the street.

Now Anna walked through the room, through the sequined sea of her classmates. Johnny the Weatherman was hurrying through the crowd. He bumped into her. "Screw everything," she heard him mutter. "Hell's bells."

"What?" she asked, startled, but he had moved on.

"Anna Green," a voice said.

She looked up.

An enormous man stood, blowing smoke out of his mouth. It was Warren; he looked as though he had been inflated, like a large balloon. He weighed probably close to three hundred pounds. His hair, which had been lush, shining ribbons of gold, had vanished. His blue gaze was familiar: fierce and bright, as though he had been trying all his life to peer through walls.

"It's your true love," he said. He laughed, and placed a large, heavy hand on her shoulder; his palm was cold.

"Warren?" she said, carefully.

"Life's been treating you good," he said.

"How are you?" she asked.

"I've been fab." He was a little out of breath. "Vance does this, Vance does that. He gets tired."

"You, tired?" Her legs felt unsteady, as though she were standing on mist.

"Arlene," he said. "My wife. Other wives break you for diamonds. She loves gold. Vance's dream house went to her earrings, her necklaces. Now we're renting a one-bedroom, no pool. Now her arm looks like Cleopatra. Who's happy?"

"You?" she asked.

He blew out a puff of foul smoke. "This could have been yours," he said. He lifted his arms. His suit fell around him like the dark wings of a bat. "Vance was a millionaire," he said. "Twice over. He built a hotel in Vegas, he sold limos. Don't underestimate him. He's going to make his fucking third million by forty."

A waitress passed carrying a tray of tiny hamburgers. "No smoking, sir," she said.

"Give me one of those, honey pie," he said. "Give me five." He shoved one into his mouth. His eyes darted around the room. "So what are you up to?" he asked.

"I'm married, living in Inland Empire. I have two kids. I repair dryers," she said.

"Well, hurray for you," he said. He drained his drink and crushed his plastic glass with his foot. "Vance needs another drink," he said, and thundered back to the bar.

She stood, watching him walk away. Johnny the Weatherman pushed by her.

"Move," he growled.

"Hey," she said. He had always moved slightly off-center, as though someone had pushed him, but now he stumbled to the center of the room with a surprising aggressiveness. He stood, watching the crowd swirl around him for a moment. Then he shoved his hand into his red sports jacket and brought out a gun.

She blinked. Had something bad happened over the last twenty years? The gun looked like a toy, and in his bright jacket, he resembled a large boy. She noticed that his hand gripped the handle in a way that seemed too comfortable; she stepped back.

"What's the weather?" Johnny yelled. "Hey! What's the weather?"

He pulled the trigger, and the bullets soared up and hit the ceiling, their explosions trembling through her throat.

A waiter scuttled toward the kitchen, holding his hand protectively over miniature quiches. Classmates hit the floor, on all fours, like dogs.

"Did it rain in Ohio?" Johnny yelled. His face was slick with sweat. Anna crouched on the maroon carpet. It was a movement new and also oddly familiar, as though she'd been secretly rehearsing it for years.

"Listen!" he yelled. She pushed her head under a chair. She wondered what idiot had sold a disabled man a gun. There was

the soft, inconceivable sound of her classmates, previously bragging about their vacation homes in Tahoe, beginning to pray.

He began to shoot. She touched her thighs and arms and realized, with surprise, how deeply she loved her body. A wineglass
exploded on the floor close to her. She cried out and pressed her
face into the musty carpet. She saw Warren Vance hunched huge-
ly on the floor. He grabbed a tiny quiche off the floor, popped it
into his mouth, and ate it. Then he ate another. Her heart trembled; suddenly, terribly, she loved him again.

A hotel security guard rushed up and shot Johnny in the chest.
The blast knocked him into the air, his feet jerking up, and then
he thudded to the floor. She could see only his hands, flung out,
delicate, perfectly still. He was dead. The fact of his deadness
amongst the careful celebration, the arranged roses, the starched
linens, was so stark it had the tenor of impoliteness; she felt ill.
The wounded cried out for help. Others crawled away, like animals, in their finery. Some bent to help the wounded, and some
fled; Anna wanted to get out. She saw Warren's large figure dash
down a hallway, and she tried to follow him. She ran out of the
hotel to the cool air and stood beside the rolling traffic on the
highway, the parade of cars. The light rose, phosphorescent, off
the highway. She could feel the rattle of the speeding cars in her
jaws.

Sirens sounded. Emergency personnel leaped out of giant
trucks. Her clothes held the odor of champagne and smoke, of a
celebration, not of a crime. She walked to her car, dazed, past the
flickering sign in the parking lot: GO TIGERS! WELCOME
CLASS of '84. She moved quickly, not realizing she was trembling
until her hand could not fit the key through the lock. She stood in
the parking lot, looking for Warren Vance. He had vanished. The
classmates clutched key rings imprinted with photos of themselves as young people; they stumbled into the night.

She drove home, two hours deep into the Inland Empire where
they lived. They lived in a community splashed onto an area that
should have remained desert, in which houses pushed aside rattlesnakes and coyotes and the newly made streets burned with an
unreal heat. It was late, and on the freeway she passed a man
shaving in his car with his interior light on, a pickup truck full of

drunken teenagers, a driver of an oil rig listening to Italian opera. Everyone drove with a giddy foolishness, obeying the traffic rules. It seemed as though they were obeying the laws of another country. She had to think carefully to remember to grip the steering wheel, to press the gas. Had she, in fact, been hit by a bullet and was now dying on her way home? She was tearful at this idea, but the notion seemed almost too convenient, cinematic, a reprieve from the life she had made with her family, which was stalwart, obedient, and exhausted.

It was almost midnight when she returned. She opened the door quietly and crept upstairs. Their house, a foreclosure, was full of holes, physically, residue of the panic of the former owners, and metaphorically, in the floor, in the walls, which they hid with couches and bookshelves and hoped someday would be repaired. Their family behaved as though they were middle-class, but realistically, with a couple skipped paychecks, an accident, a broken roof, they were on the edge of ruin. She realized she could not be shot because they could not afford to fix her.

Everyone was awake. She heard the monotone voice of her husband reading to the children. For a moment, unnoticed, she watched. Her husband appeared to be reading nursery rhymes to the stale air. The girl, who was two, was wearing a pink ball gown, and her face was smeared with red lollipop. She was climbing to the top of her brother's bunk bed and diving off it into a single pillow. The boy had emptied hundreds of cards he was collecting: Pokemon, Yu-gi-oh!, baseball and football heroes, idolatry of all persuasions, into the middle of his room, and was organizing them feverishly. The children were so tired they looked drunk, but bravely marched on.

Her husband's family had divorced bitterly when he was seven, leaving him to be raised by his grandmother, and he had marched forward with diligence and heroism, to become a social worker, to help others with their sorrow. They had met when she installed a dryer for him, and he had, like the others, asked for her ID: "Anna," he read, matter-of-factly; she had not realized until then that the suspicion of her customers caused her pain. He had been useless with his hands, just like her mother, but unlike her mother, he admired what she did. He sat beside her as she described to him the role of the wires, how they worked. He seemed full of a wonder that had escaped her, that seemed to imply a generosity toward the world; it was what caused her to marry him.

It was a guise that fell away after they married; she found that while her husband liked to give to others, he tended to want less for himself, as though that would be a dam against his own disappointment. He had said he wanted to run his own clinic, but let a colleague take over a coveted job and worked with clients who regularly bounced checks that he did not collect. He rephrased his passivity in this as generosity: "It's a loan," he said. "They'll come back when they can afford it." They never did. He sounded embattled in his compassion, as though in a constant argument. She was drawn to this, a different argument than she had been used to. When he brought her toward him, it was as though her worth were being asserted not from certainty, but by his morality.

So here they were, in their late thirties, perplexed by their own sorrow, and recently, the girl had developed a problem going to sleep. It seemed sparked by nothing: the sight of a hyena on a video, an awareness of the end of herself as a baby. She, who had fallen asleep easily before, refused to go to sleep at night. She rejected all offerings of comfort—toys, juice, songs—and stood in the blue light, screaming, as though accusing them personally of all the failings of the world. She only wanted her father in the room, and would scream violently until he sat endlessly with her. They were staggering through their days, sick with fatigue. Anna, too, felt a pull to sit forever with the child, but she felt that it was, at some level, deceitful, reassuring Anna and her husband of their own importance.

"We have to just let her cry," she had told him one night.

"How?" he said to her, to anyone who advised him to do this: "It's how she tells us how she feels." Recently, he had turned thirty-nine, the age his parents had been when they divorced, and his compassion transformed into indulgence toward the children. Now, every night, he crawled like an alligator into the little girl's bedroom. He lay on the carpet, while the girl finally fell asleep in her bed. For months, Anna had woken alone in their marital bed to find him curled up, asleep on the carpet of their daughter's room; he said he wanted the child to wake up to his face, as though to the sun.

Now it was 11:45 p.m., and her family sat in the moonlight. She watched them and did not feel quite real. It was a wonderful, airy sensation for a moment, as though she would now experience love that was blameless, unsullied.

Then she stepped into the room.

"They're still up?" she asked, an edge to her voice.

The girl looked at her and shrieked with joy. The boy jumped up. "Did you get me a toy?" he whispered, seductively, into her ear.

Anna held out her arms, and they rushed into them.

"You're back already?" asked her husband, looking suspicious.

"Something happened," she said.

"You missed us. Mommy missed us," shrieked the boy.

"Something happened," she said, again.

"She took my Harpie Lady card!" yelled the boy.

"She didn't take it," said her husband tiredly. "She found it."

"She stole it!" said the boy.

"Welcome home," said her husband. "Good night." He stood up, wandered into the parents' bedroom, and collapsed onto their bed.

"Daddy, no!" screamed the girl.

"Please, God," he muttered, hoarsely, into the bed sheets.

Anna lifted the kicking girl into her crib. "Get into bed!" she snapped at the girl.

"Daddy, help me!" screamed the girl. "Help!"

She stood, trying to stroke the girl's hair, but the child was frantic. Her rage was awesome, tremendous. Anna closed the windows so the neighbors would not hear her screams. "Please," she pleaded with the child. "For God's sake, please." The girl glared at her mother, until the father came in and stretched out on the carpet.

"You need to sleep," she said to him.

"No," he said. "Sophie, I'm here." The girl stood in her ball gown, clutching the bars of her crib, beaming.

She guided the boy into his own bed. "Look what she took!" he yelled. He opened his fist. There was a tiny shred of crumpled card in it. "Look!"

She smoothed his hair. "I'm sorry," she said.

"Get me more for my birthday," he begged. "I want to get fifty, sixty," he said. "Please." He rolled over and fell asleep.

She lay awake in the dark while the others fell into their dreams. How could they sleep? It seemed impossible, now or ever again. Was it strange that Johnny had begun to shoot? Or was it stranger that Tyra Johnson, a beauty, had gained one hundred pounds and moved to Modesto, or that Brian Horwitz, the class clown, was president of his synagogue, or that Laurie Stone, who had held her hand tenderly as they walked into kindergarten, had been indicted for embezzlement at a local bank? She looked out the window, and all she saw was determined innocence—the bullish SUVs parked in the driveways, testament to dreams of safety, of endless oil; she looked at the houses of her neighbors, flocking here, to the edge of the desert, the only place they could afford to buy in Southern California; she saw the development vanishing violently in a wildfire, in a terrorist attack. Her own childhood home was bulldozed for a luxury condo complex, her parents retired, taking medicine for their hearts, her father a math teacher now bagging groceries at Ralph's for extra money, both of them praying that Social Security would hold up. The sight of her father, a man of six feet, gentle, but bad with money, carefully guiding groceries across the parking lot, made her ache with useless love. She could not save him. The houses, their fake Spanish roofs, were slapped together with drywall and paste.

When she finally fell unconscious, she dreamed of Warren Vance. She dreamed that Warren bragged that he spent eight hundred thousand dollars on a day trip to the moon. She saw him standing on the moon's white surface in his cheap suit, smoke trailing off the end of his cigarette. "Vance wants you," he said, and pulled her toward him. She awoke to the dawn. He was nowhere. She was aroused and ashamed.

The children were first to wake. They rushed into the day with a panic, as though late for the rising of the sun. Their school-going itself seemed a joke. The children moved through the syrupy dreamtime of their childhood, while their parents could, at any moment, move them to another state, divorce, go crazy, die.

Her husband woke first and went down to make breakfast; Anna hurried to the front lawn and grabbed that day's paper. The shooting had made the front page. Eight classmates had been hurt in the shooting. She read the names of the injured; Warren Vance's was not among them.

Her husband was standing in front of the stove making bacon. The hearty smell of meat filled the air.

"Read this," she said, handing it to him.

He glanced at the newspaper. The pale morning light poured through the windows, as though shoveled from a mine of diamonds. She was pained and dazzled by its beauty. The children gnawed on strips of bacon like wolves.

Her husband looked up at her quickly.

"I was almost shot," she said, and laughed.

"You were what?" he said.

"Shot," she said.

He lifted strips of bacon from the grease to a paper towel. His hand trembled.

"Are you okay?"

"I think so."

"What did you do?"

"I hid under a chair."

He blinked. He looked at her as though through a haze.

"Did you think of throwing something at him?"

"He had a gun," she said.

He looked dissatisfied. "Did anyone try?"

"We were afraid," she said.

"My God," he said. He clutched the handle of the pan, as though trying to will all of them into an ordinary domestic scenario. Then he stepped forward and hugged her awkwardly, as if afraid to touch her body too hard. The girl hurled her bacon to the floor.

"Hot!" she announced.

"Don't throw your bacon," growled the boy.

"Stop, everyone!" Anna said. "Stop now!"

The sun made the children's hair gleam. They resumed their breakfast. Her husband looked restless.

"Was there blood?" her husband asked.

"Why are you asking me this?"

He turned quickly away, shrugged, as though caught in some thought that embarrassed him. "I wish I could have rescued you," he said.

"How?" she asked.

"Wineglasses. Knives. Thrown them at him. Distracted him. Then tripped him and hit him on the head."

He stood, encased in this fantasy of himself. "Oh," she said; she felt a primitive longing for closeness; she shuddered.

"More bacon!" yelled the boy. "Please. Now."

She had six appointments that day, and she strapped herself in the car and set off. Her car joined the flood of others on their daily missions. Her classmates had gotten hold of one another's cellphone numbers, and kept calling, urging her to help sue the Holiday Inn, to support national gun control, to establish a relationship with God. Patty Hufford, who had received 1,600 on her SATs and attended Harvard, called to announce, "I'm sorry I was mean to you in eighth grade."

"What did you say?" Anna asked Patty.

"I was mean. You wanted to do something technical and I said you were a clumsy oaf but you worked at it and now look at you and look at me," she said.

"How are you doing?" Anna asked.

"I'm not doing well," said Patty. "I never finished college. I was married to an alcoholic for ten years and finally divorced him. I think Johnny was aiming at me. I just wanted to say sorry." Patty hung up.

Anna knocked on doors, looked at circuit boards, listened for unusual noises; tightened, aligned, cleaned, lubricated parts; brought out her RF leakage detector, her thermistor vacuum gauge, her hex wrenches; she turned machines on. She noticed more in the houses than she let on—the precise cleanliness of the floors, the proliferation or absence of family photos. She listened to the way the customers talked to spouses on the phone while she worked; she wanted to hear their fear. She had always listened for it, for her parents' anxiety was imaginative, even expansive, involving bees at picnics, poisoned candy at Halloween, strangers clothed in all style of uniform; this anxiety seemed the natural order of the world.

Anna did not know the precise source of their fear, but she traced theirs (or perhaps her own) to a trip she had taken with her family and her mother's brother, his wife, and her two cousins, who were eleven and fifteen. They had gone on a camping trip and had driven home together at night. The road down the mountain had not been well lit. They had driven in a caravan down the mountain, Anna's family driving in front, and at one point Anna had looked out the back window and saw that the other car was not there. They stopped at a coffee shop and waited, and finally her parents left her with a police officer to check. She remembered sitting in the coffee shop with the officer, under-standing, on some prickly level below her skin, that her relatives were now dead. The officer was kind and solicitous and ordered whatever she wanted. Anna asked for key lime pie. Her fear and gratitude made her consume one piece of pie, then another, feel-ing each tangy sour crumb on her tongue. She began to cry, but it was not from grief yet, or shame, but for pure relief: for the feel-ing of aliveness on her tongue, for the bright green sourness and the yearning.

Her mother, in particular, was affected by the disaster; her anx-iety affected her manual dexterity. She was unable to open cans or braid hair, asking Anna to do these things, sitting, childlike, while Anna opened cans of tuna fish or tomato soup for her. While her parents wanted her to pursue a profession like theirs, a nurse and a math teacher, Anna discovered that she was skilled at fixing wiring and machinery, and she decided that she wanted to start a business repairing appliances. While she found she was also good at science and philosophy, she preferred repairing machinery, as proof that she could find a different way to relate to her life; it made her feel superior that this was concrete work that was clear, had results, solutions.

Now, in the car, returning from the day's work, she could not stop thinking about Warren Vance as a young man. She remem-bered the first time they had had sex, the frantic way he pulled her toward him, the way he had cried. She had gone to him in a daze, to be surrounded by his need. He had lived in a tiny, dark apartment with his mother, for his father was dead and he lived virtually alone; his mother was out, working as a telemarketer fifty hours a week, and the house was covered with the dust of someone who did not want to look at how she lived. Warren's room was always clean. It was plastered with cut-out pictures of famous leaders who had risen from difficult circumstances. The apartment was a shoddy, barely furnished place, but it seemed holy with them in it. He did not have a particular career goal, but wanted to assume the top post of various organizations: the head of Coca-Cola, the Governorship of California, the Presidency of the United States.

She saw the cars lining up in front of her. Now she was here; she had made it to this life. She clutched the steering wheel so hard her hands ached. Her head ached; she was suddenly so lonely it was hard to breathe.

Her cellphone rang.

"Hey, Annie," Warren Vance said, in a soft voice.

She met him, two days later, a hundred miles away. She told the babysitter she would be working late; it was absurdly easy to arrange. He wondered if she would meet him at his work. He said he wanted to talk business.

The sky was white above the freeway, cleaving the land beneath it. She did not question why she was rearranging her day to meet Warren Vance; she merely felt the swift motion of the car. It was as though she were being pulled along by a great, relentless current, as though her body craved only this: a direction.

She turned off the freeway into an industrial area, aluminum warehouses lining the empty streets. Vance's office was located in a storefront in a crumbling mini-mall. There were no trees on the block, giving the street an eerie sense of infinite sky. His office was bordered by a dirty Subway sandwich franchise and a Family Dollar store. There was the general sense that people had fled the area, as though there were an impending disaster: hurricane, famine, war.

When she walked into Vance Real Estate, she noticed that he had a steel desk balanced on a tennis ball on one side, a glass coffee table with a crack in it, and that the ventilation between this office and the Subway store was so faulty the room smelled of boiled ham. Taped on the windows were posters of palatial homes perched in glamorous destinations: Beverly Hills, Paris, Monaco. She was startled by the dinginess of the room, its contrast to who he had proclaimed he would be, but she guarded against disappointment. That would lead to the indulgence of pity; it would show her as a fool.

He was sitting in his chair, which was made of a maroon material that resembled leather. "Anna," he said, standing up. "How are you? Been too long!"

He stood, towering over her, and shook hands firmly, as though closing a business deal. She felt her hand vanish into his. She closed her eyes, for she wanted to feel longing. It was a gift; it gave her a way to feel. She was encased in the moment, perfectly still. Then he released her, and she felt the cool air again surround her hand.

"This is where you work?" she asked, concerned.

"Temporary," he said. "Renovations at the main office."

He was a little out of breath.

"How are you?" she asked.

"Fine. Vance is always fine," he said.

"I heard that Sandra Scone lost an eye," she said, quickly. "They don't know if Carl Blandon will ever walk again—"

"Eh," he said, waving this away.

"Don't you care?" she asked.

"They got in his way."

"What do you mean?" she asked, excitedly.

"Vance knew better," he said, proudly.

She looked at his large, heavy face, the pores of his skin mottled like the peel of an orange. "Come on. Weren't you scared?" she asked.

He shrugged. "Fear's a luxury," he said. He clapped his hands. "Margie," he called. "Bring some coffee out for my first love."

A girl with yellow hair so dull it looked gray came out of the back. She had the overly obedient manner of someone who had recently been released from an institution. Smiling, she held out a Styrofoam cup with some instant coffee. An extra tooth was growing out of the top of her gum like a fang.

"Margie's been with me—two years," he said.

"Usually I work in the Subway," said Margie.

"Ha, ha," he said, clapping his hands together loudly. "It's been too long. Sit down. Let me look at you. Glowing. You define the term—"

"Oh, please," she said, wanting him to go on.

"Others—not so good. Georgia Haring? Sun damage. Looked like a leather suitcase. Brian Smith? Bald as an egg."

This appeared to be unchanged, his certainty about others' failings, as though that hostility gave him a clear view of humanity. His confidence amid the bareness, the dirty windows, calmed her.

"What do you do here?" Anna asked.

"Vance is a real estate agent," he said.

"For what?" she asked.

"Glamour properties. Lots. From bitter divorces. No money down. Good deals. Why should only the rich live like kings?" He set some brochures out on his desk. She picked up one: a half-acre, beachfront, near Santa Barbara.

"That's a good one," he said. "Rock star caught with seven assistants, quote unquote, wife sues him for every penny, he's trying to get rid of this lot before she learns about it. Quick. One million dollars, he's unloading it for a cool hundred. From heartbreak comes opportunity."

They sat together in the gray fluorescent light. Warren's voice was hoarse with the same excitement as it had when he had been a young man. The sameness of his voice, its stubborn ignorance of the passing of the last twenty years, moved her. How had he managed to preserve this enthusiasm within himself? She felt the vibrations of the cars hurtling down the freeway, and she did not want to join them.

He showed her more expensive properties. Her thoughts turned to herself and how she wanted to rescue Warren Vance from this bare office. She wanted to take his large hand and lead him to a new office high in a skyscraper with enormous, pristine windows, the sun gilding the room. They would gaze out of the windows at the endless sky, and with this gesture, she would reveal all of her own goodness.

She sat, hands clasped. A voice in the adjoining room cried out for a turkey sandwich. Warren was lining up photos of beaches, of vineyards, on his desk like cards in a deck. "How long you been married?" he asked her.

"Eight years," he said.

"I've been hitched for fourteen," he said.

"Oh," she said, competitiveness reshaping itself as disdain; perhaps this was how he had ended up here.

"How is your wife?" she asked, lightly.

"Great. Hot. We're off to Cozumel. Next week." He whipped out a wallet and handed her a photo. She had expected to see a thin, glamorous starlet type, as though that would justify her jealousy, but the woman was perfectly ordinary, with a Dorothy Hamill haircut, purple sweatsuit, plump arms.

"Why did you marry her?"

"She said yes." He howled with laughter. "We went to the Riviera last year. A dream, Anna, my life is a grand dream—"

"How did you get out?" she asked.

"Hard work," he said. "Vance turned down no offers, he shook hands—"

"No," she said. "Out of the hotel."

"Oh, that," he said. "Hands and knees. Like a goddamn dog. Vance keeps his eyes open. His momma taught him that. Ha! She taught him by not giving a fuck about him. I got out on my hands and knees." He paused, slightly out of breath. "Anyone can do it. Me. You."

He was gazing at her, squinting, his eyes bright and his mouth just smiling. He leaned across his desk. "I have a secret," he said. "Don't limit yourself. Reach. Grab what you can."

"Like what?" she asked.

"Move, Anna Green. Don't just sit. That's how Vance got out of there."

There was the faint, sad blast of a truck's horn on the freeway. She felt its rumbling in the walls. Warren Vance tilted back in his fake leather chair and lovingly examined a photo of a cliff overlooking a pure blue sea. "Wouldn't you love to live here? Malibu. Fall asleep to the sound of waves."

"Someday," she said.

"What if we had been here, Annie. You and me?" he murmured.

The husky intimacy of his voice intrigued and frightened her. She looked at her watch; she had a two-hour drive home.

"I've got to go," she said.

"Wait," he said. He stood up. "Hey. Call anytime. Been too long!"

She walked slowly to the door. When she turned, he was standing, like an enormous, discarded boy, arms dangling; her heart rose with sympathy.

"I'll think about it," she said and drove the hundred miles home.

As she drove home, she remembered the first house she had walked into as a professional technician, the way an elderly woman had brought a damp, musty bra out of a broken dryer and said, "Help," and how she had felt recognized for the pure difference that was her. She loved the fact that she could turn on clients' machines and restore to the wet clothes a kind of civility, even grace. It gave her an illusion of superiority, but was it any answer? It would not protect her from death—neither would marital love, success, stability, parenthood. She was suddenly filled with loathing for her customers, their petty demands. She wanted them to shut up so she could think about Warren Vance. She thought about the yellowish office, the smell of meat floating from the next room. She imagined herself drawing the blinds so it would be dim and quiet, so they would not hear the rush of the cars. She imagined sitting on Vance's large lap, and him holding her body aloft over his enormous one, not even caressing her but admiring her breasts, her skin, her eyes.

Two hours of these thoughts amid rush-hour traffic made her head feel light and dizzy. When she returned home, she felt unreal, the way she had when she returned from the shooting, but now she also felt embarrassed. She hurried inside to find her husband at the kitchen table with the children. They were digging into a supermarket pizza. The ceiling lamp cast a stale glow upon them. She walked into the room briskly, holding out presents she had purchased earlier for the children.

"Hello!" she said. She said to the boy, "Hey. I got you a new pack of Yu-gi-oh! cards."

He looked at the pack and said, "I don't collect Yu-gi-oh! anymore. Only Pokemon." His facial expression had become slightly condescending, as though he had finally, after much searching, decided on the superior object to collect. He patiently handed them back to her.

"Oh," she said. She turned to the girl. "And here, I got you—a pink pony!"

The girl violently slapped the pony away. "I hate pink! I want yellow!" she declared.

The children's faces appeared more fleshy and solemn in the kitchen light. They had changed over the course of the day. It was something she generally noticed over weeks, months, the way their faces, arms, legs became larger, the way they acquired skills, but suddenly Anna noticed the small, precise shifts that had happened even that afternoon. Carefully, she took her seat at the table with them.

"You want cheese or pepperoni?" her husband asked. There was a new streak of gray in his hair.

"Cheese," she said.

"Did you know," said her son, as though lecturing to a college class, "that earth is mostly water?"

"Really?" she said.

"It is true," he said, and bit off a large piece of pizza.

She did not know what to say. Their faces looked so innocent—of the trip she had made that day, of their inexorable march toward adulthood, old age, their passing, she was overcome with a tender feeling toward them. She could do nothing. Her helplessness—at their growth, at her tumble toward Warren Vance—overcame her, and she began, quietly, to cry; she pretended she was coughing. Her family stared at her. They proceeded with their pizza. The girl jumped up and climbed into her lap. "I'm sorry," she said.

"She learned it today," the boy said, "but I already know that."

"I'm sorry," the girl said, over and over, delighted with the word.

The night fell upon their neighborhood. The sky faded, and the houses all filled with light. The children were bathed, dried, their teeth brushed, and eventually it was time for them to settle into their beds. Already the children were formed, moving into their lives with distinct approaches and confidence. The boy pored over his new cards as though they would tell him everything about his future, and then abruptly fell asleep. She read a story to the girl and kissed her and placed her in the crib. The girl clutched her wrist and looked up at her with accusing eyes.

"I want juice," she demanded.

This request was filled.

Then: "I want my blue pony."

"Lion."

"Pink bear."

Her husband tried to fill all requests—first kindly, with a soft voice, and then, by the thirty-minute mark, with the silence of a slave. Finally, he settled himself in a corner of her room. Anna watched her husband sitting there, pretending to look at a newspaper, to appear occupied, but it was a futile gesture—there was no light.

Anna crawled in beside him.

"It's enough," she said.

He looked at her.

"You can't just sit here forever," she said.

"You want her to sit in the dark, screaming?"

"We'll tell her we're here."

He looked at her with an eager expression, as though he believed he had just invented something. "Listen," he said, "do you think that someone can learn to live a life without fear?"

It was how he had spoken when they had met.

"How?" she asked.

"What if we gave her everything? What if she felt so loved she wasn't afraid?"

The girl's pastel ponies and kittens and bears regarded them from their perches.

"But you can't sit here your whole life," she said, carefully.

He sighed sharply, and stared at the air. "Sometimes I think you don't know anything about me," he whispered. "What am I thinking right now?"

"Tell me."

"I have reservoirs of goodness you don't see."

"Like what?"

"I want to help people on a national scale. I want to drive trucks around the country feeding the hungry."

A sheer curtain lifted and fell with a breeze from the window, as though the curtain was trying to breathe.

"Crowds will come up to my truck and carry out bread and milk and when I leave they will applaud," he said.

"Okay," she said, puzzled.

"I sit here and plan," he said. "Sometimes I don't think you look at me the right way."

"What is the right way?"

"As though you see my goodness," he said.

She thought, suddenly, of Warren Vance's naked body. He was not only wide, but was surprisingly tall, his head almost touching the ceiling. Warren wrapped his arms around her and began nuzzling her neck. She closed her eyes, trying to get the thought of him out of her head.

She looked at her husband, his long legs stretched in front of him. She understood, suddenly, that when they married, they pledged not only to love each other in the future, but to remedy the past—to give each other what they had not had as children. He had wanted his loneliness to be recognized; she had wanted proof of her own value. Now they tried to disguise themselves as adults by preparing meals, having sex, driving cars; but they sat beside each other, their old needs stubborn, jabbing.

"I want to," she said.

"Okay," he said.

They sat, frozen, beside each other. The girl was finally asleep. Anna reached over and clasped his hand. She felt the pulse of his heart in his palm.

Three days later, she was making dinner, when the phone rang.

"Annie," said Warren. "You never call. You never write."

She stood against the counter; she felt pinned, even though she was the only one in the room.

"Been thinking about you," he sang. "Been thinking about that girl in auto shop who could take apart a carburetor faster than any of them. Remember her?"

The children were in the living room, watching the television with fevered expressions. "I guess," she said.

"That girl should be standing on a cliff watching the sun set on her personal slice of the Pacific," he said. "Would you believe ten grand?"

She could taste his voice in her mouth. "I don't know," she said.

He cleared his throat. "What did you think of Vance, Anna? Be honest."

"Why?"

"Should Vance have had children, Anna? Tell him. His wife didn't want to. Should Vance have gone to business school? Maybe Vance should have learned Russian. Arabic. Vance could catch Osama bin Laden—" He was short of breath. "Vance can't fucking move."

His anxiety alarmed her. "Maybe you could try Slim-Fast," she said.

"Do you know that I am the fattest man in my zip code," he said, sadly. "I like all cuisines. I hate nothing."

It was dusk. The windows glowed. She moved from the refrigerator to the microwave, defrosting meat. She held the phone to her ear.

"Tell me what you used to tell me," he said. "After."

Her heart jumped. "What are you talking about?"

"You know."

She remembered when she was eighteen years old and lying naked beside him, the experience of love so new that she felt she had been taken apart and reassembled. She closed her eyes and spoke to him, a soft, obscene endearment.

"Say it again," he whispered.

She did. The moment felt clear and full.

"You say it," she said.

He said the word to her. She closed her eyes and breathed. The air was warm. Where was the person she had been? She remembered how she sat in the coffee shop, looking at the cakes revolving in a glass column, the taste of lime and sugar on her lips, while she waited for her parents to tell her of the deaths in her family. She remembered how her parents rushed in after they had seen the accident to claim her. She remembered their eyes as they saw her, fierce with gratitude for her presence, and also fearful. The fear resembled suspicion, and that was what she had remembered.

"Thank you," he said, solemnly. "You are a gem, you know?"

She was frightened. The kitchen looked drained of light.

"Be good to yourself," he said.

"I have to go," she said.

"Wait," he said. "Don't go."

She clutched the phone and listened to his breath.

"Let me get you a deal," he said, softly.

She laughed. Hearing this, a business offer, after she had spoken to him the way she had twenty years before, was so absurd it was a relief. "Oh, right," she said.

"Grab what you can," he whispered. "No money down. Investment in the future."

She thought of herself, her family standing on a cliff together looking at a sunset. Her guilt at speaking to Vance so intimately made her want to do something generous for her family, as though that would absolve her.

"I can even take credit cards," he said.

She read him her Visa number, slowly, and he wrote it down.

"Thank you," he said. "You've made the right decision. Vance will call back in a couple days." He hung up.

Two days passed, then three. She did not tell anyone about her sudden purchase of a beachfront lot. She had not wanted one particularly before, but she began to think about it, became excited about the cliff overlooking the sunset. Here they were, in this space of time together, and perhaps it should be spent in a way that confirmed their nobility, in a castle overlooking the sea.

She picked up her phone quickly whenever it rang.

A week went by.

She did not hear from Warren Vance. Her credit-card bill arrived. She had allegedly purchased five hundred and forty-eight dollars worth of gourmet steaks from Wisconsin, twelve hundred and thirty-four dollars worth of airline tickets via Orbitz, and three thousand two hundred and eighty-four dollars worth of watches at Cartier.

She stood, trembling, reading his longings. Then she tried to call him, but the number was dead.

The next day, she told the babysitter to stay late and sped out to his office after she made her appointments for the day. She drove too fast, feeling the rush of the cars, passing the gray trees, the silver brush on the golden hills, the endless, burgeoning developments. She needed only this—the craving for direction. The sound of her breath was deafening.

She turned the car into the parking lot where his office had been. A couple young, bulky blond men were carrying mattresses into his office. She ran toward them.

"Where's Vance Real Estate?" she asked.

"This here's Ed's Beds. No one here by that name."

Panic fluttered through her. She ran into the Subway outlet. Margie was at the register, her hair now arranged in a net.

"Where's Warren Vance?" Anna asked.

Margie's eyes flashed, as though the name woke her up. "The fat guy?"

She nodded.

"The fucking jerk. He said he'd give me forty bucks for saying I was his secretary, bringing coffee, smiling, et cetera, and then one day he didn't show. Where is he? Do you know?"

Anna rushed out of the store into the parking lot. The sky was dark blue and ribbed with silver clouds. She clutched her cellphone, but there was no one she could call. She stood alone under the sky as it faded and cooled, and it took her a long time before she returned to her car.

It took her three days to tell her husband about the credit card. This was what she told him: she had been buying shoes at Sears; she left her wallet at the store and hurried back; in that time, someone must have copied down her card number. She had been victimized; it was the easiest thing to say.

"Five hundred dollars of steaks?" he said. "Did this idiot eat a whole cow?" He paused. "What else did you leave there? Our address? Our bank account?"

She realized that she was drawn to his moral quality because she was always waiting to be judged.

"It was an accident," she said.

"What's going on?" he said, his voice tense.

"Nothing."

"You're not telling me the truth," he said. He put the credit-card bill down. "What was it like in that room?" he asked.

"What room?"

"The reunion. I want to know."

She closed her eyes. What could she tell him? She remembered the musty odor of the hotel carpet, the sudden beauty of Warren Vance wolfing down the mini-quiches. She thought of how she had hunched under the chair, listening to the bullets, how their sound had ached in her jaws.

"It was terrible," she said.

"Did you think about the children?" he asked.

"No."

"Your parents?"

"No."

"Did you think about me?"

She paused. "No."

He stepped back.

"Why not?"

"I thought about myself," she said; it was all that her mind had, at that moment, been able to hold.

Was this a terrible truth about her? Did it say something that her last thought would have been about herself? Would others have been more generous, or would their love have limits, too?

When she had run outside, there had been this stunning gladness, as though she were rushing into cool rain. The light rose, pale, radiant, off the freeway. She surveyed it all, hoping that she deserved it.

"Well," he said, his tone aggrieved. "All right."

They stood in silence for a moment.

"I would have thought of myself, too," he said. "I know it."

Relief fell open like a flower inside her. "Why?" she asked.

"I don't know," he said. "No one else did. Thirty years ago, no one did. Do you know that when I was nine, I couldn't stand the dark?" he said. "My parents had divorced. I was living with my grandmother. I had to keep my light on. My grandmother kept turning it off. I woke up in the dark, and I thought I was dead. When I turned on the light, I looked at my hands and squeezed them to make sure they were here."

How perfectly could they recognize each other's sadness? It was the imperfection that they had married and pledged to care for. She felt his sadness echo in her, and that echo was a relief; she stepped toward him and kissed him. His hands grabbed her shoulders as though they were both floating, moving without gravity through the air. She fell into him, their shared, monstrous longings, and they gripped each other in the fragile, lit box that was their house, holding each other with forgiveness, this place that they had landed, here.

Two weeks later, she picked up the phone.

"Annie," he said. His voice crackled.

"Warren Vance?" she shouted. "Where the hell are you?"

"Kuala Lumpur. Buenos Aires. Singapore. Vance gets around," he said.

"You thief!" she said. "I'm going to find you."

"No you won't," he said. "Because Warren Vance is dead."

"You are not," she said.

"Warren Vance died twenty years ago, in his momma's arms," he said. "Who are you to say who is alive and who isn't?"

"Stop!" she yelled. "Don't say that!"

"Thank you," he said, softly. "Thank you for believing in me. Thank you for the watches. Thank you for the steaks. Do you know how rarely I get steaks? They were delicious. You gave Vance your Visa. That shows trust. You're a good person."

She was out of breath.

"Why?" she asked. "Why did you do this?"

"Vance takes care of himself," he said. "It's his first goal and his second."

There was a crackle, and then he was gone.

The lights went on in Anna's house each night, as they went on in the other houses on their street. The houses clung to the arid hills, temporarily finding a foothold in the brush. One night, Anna told her husband they had to tell their daughter good night and then leave the room while she fell asleep. He looked at her coldly, as though she were a stranger, and then surprisingly agreed, as though he wanted to be led to a new place. Anna kissed the girl's hair. The girl stared at them, her eyes dark and burning. What would give each of them the most dignity? The parents, the child, how did they fool themselves into strength?

The girl screamed for twenty-three minutes, and then fell asleep.

The next morning, the girl stood up in her crib. "I awake," she said. Her tone was matter-of-fact. She stood in the fresh light, gazing at Anna eagerly. Anna stumbled toward her and lifted her out. The girl kicked softly in the air.

"You did it," she whispered to the girl. She tried to say it grandly. What words would convey a love that would carry her forward? The girl was bored, wriggled in her arms, looking for her toys. The morning spread out, glazed and damp and blue, outside the windows. Anna clutched the girl's soft, living weight against her chest.

The lights went out in Anna's house every night. The boy abandoned all cards to focus his attention on soccer. The girl decided to eschew princesses to become a witch. She sat at the dinner table wearing a pointy black hat.

Each night, she and her husband lay in their bed. Her husband's arm came over her body at night, and she held it. One night, she whispered to him the intimacy she had spoken to Warren Vance, so softly she did not know if he heard it. His face twitched with surprise; he said the word back softly, and pressed his face against hers. They all huddled together in a truce of their longings, in an island of time together before they would all separate again.

Occasionally, Warren Vance came to her in her dreams. He stood on a bright bluish moon and called to her, "Get Vance." She held on to him, kissed him ferociously, trying to taste all of him before he let her go.

JILL GILBRETH

When the Stars Begin to Fall

I.

The men and women of the Causon Creek Church of God with Signs Following were expecting families from congregations all over the South to attend their annual homecoming services, some from hundreds of miles away. Most would cross the Tennessee border from North Carolina, Virginia, and Kentucky, though a few were coming from states as far away as Alabama and Florida. When they arrived they would call each other *brother* and *sister,* and they would greet each other with a "holy kiss." Like the members of the Causon Creek congregation, they believed in the Father and the Son and the Holy Ghost, and they practiced this belief through strict interpretation of the scriptures of the Bible, including the sixteenth chapter of the Gospel of Mark: *And these signs shall follow them that believe; in my name shall they cast out devils; they shall speak with new tongues; they shall take up serpents; and if they drink any deadly thing, it shall not hurt them; they shall lay hands on the sick, and they shall recover.* They believed that when they received the power of the Holy Ghost, a gift they called the anointing, they were protected from the deadly effects of fire and strychnine and from the poison of venomous snakes. When a man or woman died following these "signs," it was often considered an act of God's will. Every day was lived as if it might be the last. As if the stars might fall from the heavens at any moment.

II.

The sound came from somewhere in between the back of Robert Patterson's tongue and the insides of his ears. At first a single half-human syllable, it jerked his head forward and divided, escaping his lips in triplicate, like a protest from a faulty ignition.

A swift silence filled the room. Robert let go of a grin and caught his breath as the congregation waited for him to begin his sermon. He didn't need to know what to say next. He had only to keep his mind on God. When he had his mind in that right place, that was when the spirit moved him, and in its presence he'd take up any deadly thing. The current of energy that had taken root at the base of his skull traveled to his arms and legs. It was on its way: powerful, inexplicable sensation. A chorus of rattles erupted from the large wooden box on the floor near the foot of the pulpit. Robert shuffled his feet and slouched, urging his body into descent. The pupils of his eyes swelled beneath their lids as he reached into the box of serpents.

Again, he stuttered.

His wife, Rachel, who had been sleeping peacefully beside him and who was accustomed to hearing strange utterances from her husband's mouth, pleaded with consciousness for a few more hours of rest. In the morning she would wake up earlier than usual, along with the other women in the congregation who had been up the night before preparing breads and casseroles and cakes for the families soon to arrive. Those traveling from greater distances would be there after the morning service, in time to finish the remains of the afternoon supper on the church grounds, or by nightfall to attend the evening service. The men of the congregation had also worked ahead of time to prepare for the homecoming event. Meetings had been held to discuss the use of church funds to help families who wanted to attend, but were struggling financially. Folding tables had been gathered and transported for the afternoon potluck. Robert and the other elders had just finished putting an overdue coat of paint on the church, wherein he was now offering his imaginary sermon.

Robert's dog was sprawled out on the floor next to his side of the bed, and as the third wave of nonsense broke, he pulled himself up on all fours and gave his head a shake, rattling his chain collar. With this, Robert thought he heard someone say *Amen,* and he rose from his pillow in a dazed state.

Rachel opened her eyes and remembered their two little girls in the next room. "Robert," she whispered. "Robert, go back to sleep." It took a moment for her eyes to adjust to the darkness. He was upright.

Robert looked down at his wife, perplexed, muttering something about what a fine service it was and had she seen Jacob?

"Jacob's at John and Sarah's," she answered. The boy had arrived earlier that week, two inches taller and in need of a haircut. He'd slept on their living room floor until John and Sarah Bishop's three young boys enlisted him to help them build a summer fort.

"What's he doing there?" Robert asked.

Rachel sat up and studied her husband's face. He was nowhere near awake. "He's in bed, asleep. Like you should be."

"He's tired out," Robert said.

"Yes, I imagine he is," Rachel offered.

Robert closed his eyes, and Rachel said something he couldn't decipher. Her words seemed to disappear somewhere in the clearing behind the church. He searched the landscape as if to try and find them, until he felt something moving in the grass. It was his own two feet. He was walking with one hand level on his brow, in an effort to block the sun. Jacob was standing in front of the oak tree. Its dead branches were adorned with empty glass bottles that were swaying despite the absence of a breeze. One of its limbs cradled a large black rattlesnake. Robert looked at the boy, almost a man now, and saw himself at sixteen.

"In the Garden of Eden it stood up on two legs," Robert said. "Like a man."

"I'm going take it up," said Jacob.

"You're not afraid?"

The snake sounded its rattle.

"Who hung up all these bottles, Jacob?"

"You did," he answered.

"Why'd I do that?"

"They need to be filled," said Jacob. The rattlesnake slid down the tree and onto the boy's shoulder. Jacob propped its head up with the back of his hand. "Like you."

III.

Rachel and the girls were finishing breakfast when Robert walked into the kitchen, his hair still damp from the shower. Signs of last-minute food preparation covered the countertops: boxes of aluminum foil and cellophane, spare platters, and serving utensils. Newly washed dishes stuffed the draining board. She'd been up for hours and hadn't woken him.

"Sit down, I'll fix you an egg," Rachel said. She poured him a cup of coffee.

Robert opened the refrigerator and poked through the items she'd made for the potluck. "John and I have something to take care of before the service," he said.

Rachel gave him the coffee and sat back down at the table. She still had to get their daughters dressed and out of the house. Robert closed the refrigerator and stood there for a moment sipping at his coffee and staring at the three of them.

Three girls, he thought. John and Sarah had boys coming out of their ears.

"I thought you had to go," said Rachel. She handed him a napkin for the chicken leg he'd stolen.

"If John calls, tell him to wait," he said, dumping his coffee in the sink.

At the café, he found John sitting with Carl Evans, the senior elder of the church. The waitress poured Robert a cup of coffee and topped off John and Carl's cups before going to check on her other customers. A group of men wearing fishing gear entered the coffee shop. Robert noticed the sheriff's vehicle parked near the entrance as the men were ushered toward a booth. The subject of conversation shifted rapidly from good weather to the likelihood of police presence at the service.

"You know as well as I do he'll come," said John.

"Let him," Robert said.

Tennessee had been the first state to prohibit the practice of snake handling in church. The law had been in place for over fifty years but was rarely enforced. Holiness people were usually left alone with their beliefs unless, as happened remarkably seldom, a bite proved fatal, but the service that resulted in the death of Jacob's parents had been a particularly bizarre one, and the headlines had haunted them for months.

They'd gone to Kentucky to attend a service in a newly established church. Jacob's father and mother were good friends with a few of the members of the new congregation, and his grandmother lived nearby, in Louisville. Robert had driven down with the family. The new church was situated in an abandoned strip mall. The serpent boxes sat untouched for most of the service, but a few members of the new congregation had also brought jars of lemonade that were laced with strychnine. When the service seemed to be coming to an end, a new member opened one of the boxes and removed three copperheads. He began to pass them around, and Jacob's parents backed away from the pulpit. The man then removed a jar of the lemonade from the pulpit and took it over to Jacob's parents. Robert watched as they drank the liquid. When the authorities questioned members of the congregation the next morning, they learned that Jacob's parents had both suffered multiple bites and had ingested a strychnine solution that was more deadly than the snake venom.

Now, a sheriff's officer passed Robert and John and took a seat at the counter two places down from Carl. He nodded at the three of them, and John and Carl returned the gesture. Robert pursed his lips and glanced at his coffee. Carl finally broke under the silence.

"You know, officer," he said, "I heard the other day that in this county, it's illegal to snare a fish with a lasso."

"Is that right?" the officer asked.

"It's what I hear, anyway," Carl said.

Robert stood up and pulled his wallet from his pocket. He paid for their coffee and got up to leave. John gave Carl a pat on the shoulder and tossed a tip on the counter.

IV.

Sarah was on the porch with the baby when Rachel and the girls arrived. The plan had been for Rachel to bring what she prepared for the potluck to Sarah's house because it was closer to the church. As usual, Rachel had cooked too much food.

"There's more," Rachel said. The girls handed off the boxes of food wrap Sarah had asked them to bring and ran back down to the car. Sarah's boys were playing in the backyard with Jacob. Their voices rang out from behind the house as the women made their way inside. "Have you lost your mind yet?" Rachel asked.

"Not yet. But there's still plenty of day left." Sarah took the food wrap and deviled eggs to the kitchen table and opened the refrigerator door. "Jacob being here's been a big help." She shifted the baby to her other hip and moved a few items around to make room.

The girls appeared with two more plates and were sent out to play with a reminder to keep their clothes neat. Rachel put the last item in the refrigerator and closed the door. "How's he seem to you?" she asked.

"Jacob?" Sarah asked. She handed the baby to Rachel. He fussed immediately. "He's all right, I suppose. He's less confused than I expected." Three pies sat on the counter next to the oven, two of them covered. Sarah whipped a sheet from the borrowed box of foil and carefully wrapped the third one.

"How do you mean, less confused?" Rachel bounced gently with the baby toward the window in an attempt to hush him. The baby looked at his mother and sputtered.

"Well, it's been almost a year since he moved away," Sarah answered. "Lord knows what his grandmother's been filling his head with." Sarah held out her arms and smiled with her whole face. The baby reached for her and kicked his legs, wildly.

Jacob's paternal grandmother had been given guardianship after his parents died. The woman had never approved of her son's religious beliefs. When the time came to let the congregation know whether he would be at the homecoming, she told Jacob that he would have to make the decision on his own.

"Being here will do him some good," said Rachel. "The woman knows it or she wouldn't have let him come."

The women gazed out the window for a moment. Jacob entered the kitchen, limping. He had woken with a smarting hip, which was made worse roughhousing with the Bishop children. A small boy caught up with him and jumped on his back, forcing him to stop, hands to knees.

"I have you now, mister!" the boy shouted.

"Hey, Mrs. Patterson," said Jacob.

"Hey, yourself!" said the boy, hanging on.

"Jeremiah," said Sarah. "Get down and go use a comb on your hair. I'm not telling you a third time." Jeremiah got off Jacob's back, reluctantly and dramatically, and went upstairs for his comb. Sarah was about to ask Jacob to call the other boys inside when she heard the truck outside. "Sounds like Robert's truck," she said.

"It is," Rachel confirmed, moving to the window to watch it pass. "Honestly, they're like little boys."

"Yes, they are," said Sarah. "I think John's looking forward to today more than the kids are, and they're pretty wound up."

"Robert said the snake they're after is a real beauty," said Jacob.

Rachel and Sarah both turned around.

"They're hunting a snake?" Rachel asked.

"Yeah," Jacob said. "Robert asked me if I wanted to help them, and I would have, but you'd already asked me to help out with the boys." This was a half-truth. The idea terrified him.

"Well, I appreciate that," said Sarah. "Would you mind calling the rest of the kids inside?"

"Sure," he said. "I hope I didn't get anyone in trouble."

Rachel patted Jacob on the back. "Don't you worry about it," she said. "You didn't tell me anything I wouldn't have guessed."

Sarah waited for Jacob to leave the kitchen. "Did you know that Robert asked him to go with them?"

"No," Rachel said. "Robert's not like John. He doesn't tell me everything. I either have to try to read his mind or read between the lines at least." She wasn't surprised Robert had asked him to go. Jacob had just turned sixteen, and he seemed to know as well as everyone that there was nothing to be said that could explain what happened to his parents. The only answer anyone could give Jacob or each other was the one Robert seemed to be working out in his sleep the night before. It was God's will. Robert was doing his best to show him how important it was to trust that. This was his way.

v.

John followed Robert along the hillside toward an outcropping of rocks that had often proved a good place to find rattlesnakes. The rocks got the early morning sun, and according to Robert the warmth attracted the best snakes for handling. The big ones, he had said, survive the cold. John had not seen the black diamond rattlesnake they were after, but he took Robert's word that it was worth making a last-minute effort.

Catching the snake took some doing. Robert had lifted the rock it was under a bit awkwardly, and John misjudged its path. The snake nearly got away before John pinned its head to the ground with a lead pipe.

"You got a good grip on him?" Robert asked.

John thought about the snake. A big son of a gun. It was the same shade as the dirt it was thrashing in. "As good as I'm gonna get," he said. It was sounding its rattle. "Get him quick. He's not too happy."

Robert bent down and tried using a hook to scoop its tail into a burlap sack, but the snake whipped its body from the sack as soon as it made contact with it.

"I don't know," John said. His right arm was so focused on keeping its head under control that it had locked. "We might not be able to get this one."

They had already caught more snakes than they had the need for. Robert had begun to trap them as soon as the weather warmed up, in anticipation of the homecoming, but John knew Robert well enough to know that getting this particular snake was a matter of pride. He had heard Robert bragging the other day about how many he had caught that spring, and how he still had his eye on a black rattler.

Robert dropped the hook on the ground and slid the burlap sack under the snake's tail and midsection. "Too bad Jacob's not here," he said. "We could use a third man."

"You could have asked Carl," John said. "Anyways, I'd say Jacob is still more boy than man."

"Jacob's a bit more grown up than you think he is," Robert said. After the snake calmed down a little, Robert reached for the hook. "Are you ready to let go of his head?" he asked.

John looked at Robert. He didn't want to release it. Before he could say so, Robert abruptly grabbed the lead pipe from John's hand and used the hook to force the snake's head into the burlap sack.

"I've got you—" said Robert. He dropped the pipe and held the sack at arm's length. The snake writhed at the bottom of it. "You're stubborn, but I've gotcha."

Robert carried the snake to the truck. John reached for the lead pipe. It was a risky thing his friend just did, he thought. Robert was usually more levelheaded than that. The homecoming would be more emotionally charged than usual because of what had happened last year in Kentucky, and John was beginning to wonder if Robert would act just as recklessly during the services, if he would put Jacob at risk. The boy had told him the night before, after he and Sarah had put the kids to bed, that Robert spoke to him about the first time he handled a snake. Given what he had been through, John thought that it was enough that he had held on to his faith. The last thing Jacob needed was to be pressured into handling. That Robert meant well for the boy was certain, but John questioned his judgment.

VI.

The door to the Causon Creek Church of God with Signs Following was propped open, and the voices of its congregation drifted outside in waves among the buzzing insects, asking safety for their brothers and sisters who were still traveling, and welcoming those who had returned. A number of them had been married or baptized as members of the Causon Creek Church of God, but had later left in search of opportunity in larger towns and cities. They honored the memory of Jacob's parents, echoing sentiments offered up at their funeral the year before. "This world is not worth living in if it is not lived for the Lord," said Carl, "and if there was anyone who understood that, it was those two." The rest of the congregation gave thanks for the mercy of God's loving grace. A few visitors came forward to give their testimonies.

Jacob sat listening to the cadence of their voices along with the other sounds of the room—shoes against the floor, opened and closed hymnals, mourning doves outside. The church he and his grandmother attended now and then in Louisville was in a large, modern building. The only voice that echoed there belonged to the minister, who wore a microphone. They hardly knew the other members of the congregation.

He hardly knew people here now, outside of the Pattersons and the Bishops. Most of the boys and girls he had grown up with were seated in little groups at the back of the church. A few had come up to him before the service and tried to make conversation, asking him about Louisville and about his new school with awkward interest before walking away to gossip about him and his grandmother. The one person who didn't seem to be in with them was a girl named Anna who was two years younger than him and who he'd almost kissed once. She sat in the front row with her mother and grandmother and three younger girls, two of whom Jacob recognized as her sisters.

The Bishop children were seated between Sarah and Jacob in the third row. Jeremiah's hands were locked on the back of the next pew, his forehead resting between them. He was busy swinging his feet back and forth—together, then separately, together, then separately—counting their movements and using the highest numbers he could before starting the process all over again. He had already studied the banners posted on the church walls at least twenty times, even though he couldn't read most of what was written on them. A few were printed with verses from the Bible books of Mark and Luke. On a different banner, a word he was very familiar with appeared eight times: NO MEN WITH LONG HAIR OR MUSTACHES. NO WOMEN WITH SHORT HAIR. NO MAKE-UP. NO JEWELRY. NO LYING. NO BACK-BITING. NO NAME CALLING. NO BAD LANGUAGE.

The message above the pulpit read: THIS WORLD IS NOT MY HOME. John was standing beneath it, bringing the service that had been going on for almost three hours to a close. New arrivals filtered into the church toward the end of the service, and just about everyone expected to show was accounted for. The men gathered outside in groups talking, the volume of their voices increasing as the women busied themselves setting up lunch. The food was arranged on the tables by category, main dishes first. The children formed a line and led the way around the setup. Their mothers followed them, keeping track of the contents of their plates to ensure they weren't heaped entirely with desserts.

Robert stood toward the back of the line with Jacob. John wasn't far behind. He watched the two of them, Robert with his hand on the boy's back, leaning in as he talked, Jacob listening intently. Later in the day, John would witness them heading in the direction of Robert's truck, Jacob laughing nervously as Robert tried to convey the size of the snake they'd caught that morning, using his arms as a measure.

VII.

White light spilled from a pair of industrial-strength bulbs nestled in the eaves of the church. John stood near the entrance, blocking the glare with the palm of his hand as he greeted one last couple and directed them inside. The voices that had gradually filled the church to its rafters were abruptly reduced to a dull hum after the doors fell shut. John peered up the slope toward the makeshift parking lot. Robert and Jacob were still leaning against the bed of Robert's truck, arms folded, talking. John made his way up the slope.

"There he is," said Robert.

"We were wondering when you'd get here," said Jacob.

"Are you coming in?" John asked.

"As soon as you give us a hand," Robert answered. He turned toward the bed of the truck and released the tailgate.

Jacob followed Robert's lead and unlatched the other side. "Which one do you want?" he asked John. The black rattlesnake knocked its head against its trap. Jacob took a step back.

"Why don't you go on inside?" said John. "That fellow from Nashville is in there tuning up. I told him you might want to get a look at his new guitar."

Robert winked at Jacob and reached for one of the wooden tomato crates he used to transport snakes to services.

"Yes, sir," said Jacob, stuffing his hands in his pockets.

Robert set the crate on the ground as Jacob walked away. "Well," he said, reaching for another. "Are you going to help me here?"

"I don't know that I should," John said.

"You're serious." Robert propped his arm on the side of the truck. "You are, aren't you?"

"Yeah, I am, Robert, and here's why. Here's why. If they show up tonight—which they will, you can count on that." One of the other church elders had heard that the police were planning to come to the service.

"I am counting on it," said Robert. The church door swung open. Sarah stepped out and peered into the darkness. Musicians were tuning their instruments.

John reached for the trap with the black rattler in it and pulled it toward the edge of the tailgate. "I want you to promise me something, Robert." He looked down the slope at the church. Sarah was still standing in the doorway. "Promise you won't let him near the serpent boxes."

Robert stacked the two crates, one on top of the other. "I can't promise you that, John," he said, quietly. "I'm surprised you'd ask me to."

VIII.

Carl led the evening service with prayer requests. A collection plate was passed for a young couple from Alabama who had arrived during the afternoon supper—relatives of a member from a neighboring county who were newly wed and newly saved. They'd brought a friend. One of the church elders asked for spiritual guidance for a coworker who was seeking the Lord. A man who was moving his family out of state to take a new job asked for help in their search for a new congregation. There were relatives who were struggling with illnesses.

An old woman Carl called "mother" approached the pulpit and asked for healing for her arthritis. Rachel and two other women laid their hands on her and began to pray aloud. Others followed, standing or kneeling, some with their eyes closed, some with their hands raised to heaven. Sarah placed her baby in the charge of Rachel's daughters and attended to her restless boys before bowing her own head and asking for patience. John stepped up to the pulpit and clasped arms with Carl and Robert and joined them in prayer for a safe and joyful time in the Lord.

Jacob observed the people in the room, most of them strangers to him now. The congregation grew louder and louder until the church was swelling with clamor. It usually went on like this until one voice could be heard above all the others. A few of the men were competing for the opportunity to speak first. Eventually, everyone but Robert fell silent.

"I didn't know if the Lord was gonna move on me," he began. "Glory be."

"Glory be to God," someone replied.

"I'm just thankful to be here with you, brothers and sisters," he continued.

"Thank you, Lord Jesus," the same woman replied. Jacob now recognized her as the talkative friend who'd come with the couple from Alabama. She'd approached him at the potluck after the morning service and barely introduced herself before she told him how sorry she was about his parents. He hardly heard what Cheryl from Alabama said after that. He'd focused instead on the mound of potato salad perched dangerously close to the edge of her paper plate.

"The Lord's got me wanting to tell you something," Robert continued. "You've all heard it many times, but seeing as we're all together here I think it should be said out loud again right now what the Lord tells us about those who believe. Brothers and sisters, I'm talking about the sixteenth book of Mark. I know you're familiar."

"Yep," said Carl.

"Mark tells us something about those of us who believe," said Robert, clapping his hands at a steady pace as he spoke. "Am I in the word, Brother John?"

John nodded.

"Brothers and sisters—the Lord knows you."

"Oh yes He does," said Rachel.

"I—I—I know you know," said Robert. "I know you know what He says through Mark about those who believe!" Robert shouted. "It says in His name they shall cast out devils!"

"I've seen it happen," said Carl.

"They shall speak with new *tongues*-ah!"

"I've had that Holy Ghost," said Carl.

"They *shall* take up serpents!"

"Give me that Holy Ghost, sweet Jesus," said Carl.

And it shall not hurt them, Jacob thought.

"Not *may* or *might* but *shall*-ah!" said Robert.

That's what Jacob's father had told him, that the bites wouldn't hurt him, couldn't hurt him. He said it every time he'd drunk strychnine or received a bite, and Jacob had trusted him, though the physical effects were terrifying—the convulsions, the fever, the swollen limbs and skin that often turned black from the venom.

"Some folks don't want to live strictly by the word," Robert went on. "And then they say they *believe*-ah! They're not holding the keys to the kingdom of *God*-ah! They're holding on to this *world*-ah!"

Jacob had overheard Robert talking to his father with that same level of fury in his voice the night his parents died. Then he'd seen him hunched over his mother in disbelief. His father had lived for a few more hours, his body arching from the violent convulsions Jacob later learned were from the strychnine.

"Brothers and sisters, I'll ask you one time what it is you love about this world!"

The band began to play. Jacob stood with his arms folded,

shaking a leg to the music. The old mother clapped her hands to the pulse of the tune, keeping double time with her foot. Jeremiah sat, wide-eyed, next to Sarah. She bounced the baby on her knee.

> *Oh, Brothers, what will you do?*
> *Brothers, what will you do?*
> *Brothers, what will you do?*
> *When the stars begin to fall?*

The man and woman from Alabama got up and danced together. Cheryl threw her hands up in the air and jumped into the aisle, spinning. She fell to the ground and slapped the floor, then stood up and fainted into the arms of John.

> *I'll bid farewell to this old world.*
> *I'll bid farewell to this old world.*
> *I'll bid farewell to this old world.*
> *When the stars begin to fall.*

Someone had opened one of the serpent boxes. Robert dropped a copperhead on the floor. Carl caught it and returned it to its crate. Three or four smaller snakes were passed around the room. Rachel and Robert blessed the Alabama couple, and the husband fell to his knees and began speaking in tongues. Robert was laughing.

Jacob approached the pulpit. He had asked Robert what it felt like to experience anointing, to be in the Holy Spirit, and he'd said it was a powerful, inexplicable sensation—a pleasure and pain wrapped inside a kind of weightlessness. Robert placed a hand on Jacob, in blessing, before he opened the crate with the rattlesnake.

It was calm in Jacob's care. It wrapped its body around his arm and moved gently toward the floor. Robert kept its head up with the back of his hand. A powerful, inexplicable sensation washed over Jacob—a kind of weightlessness but without the pleasure that Robert had described. He thought of his father, who had convulsed so violently from the strychnine that he'd wrestled with Jacob in his efforts to keep him still, to demand his future. It was fear he felt now. Jacob led the rattlesnake onto Robert's shoulder. The congregation was on its feet, singing and shouting out loud and dancing when Jacob fled the church.

Republican

A section of the newspaper, rolled into a tight cone and flaming at the top, stuck out of the cook's ear the first time I saw him. This was early June, in Corpus Christi, Texas, when I was sixteen and had been hired as the delivery driver for La Cocina Mexican Restaurant. The cook was sweating. He sat cross-legged on the stove in the kitchen, eyes and fists clenched, with two waitresses beside him. One of the women was dribbling salsa into plastic to-go cups. The other fanned the blue-black smoke away from the cook's face with a laminated menu.

The night before, I'd called about the ad in the paper and was told to show up the next morning for an interview. My father made me wear his pink tie, his only tie, though I'd just expected to fill out an application and learn that I lacked adequate experience. Aside from helping out at my father's pawnshop, I'd never held a job. But there'd been no paperwork at La Cocina, no discussion of previous employment. The owner asked if I had a valid driver's license, a reliable car, any moving violations or outstanding warrants. She asked if I was an honest person, and I said, "I try to be." The answer seemed to surprise and please her, as if I'd solved a riddle that had stumped other drivers, then she told me to go into the kitchen and ask if there were any orders yet. She also told me to tell the cook that if another customer complained about the menudo tasting like beer, she'd call immigration.

When the waitress fanning the smoke saw me, she said, "Bathroom's down the hall."

"I work here," I said.

The cook's head was parallel to the floor, the smoke from the newspaper ribboning toward the grease-blotched ceiling. He wore a mustache and a V-neck T-shirt. A half-empty beer bottle sat next to him on the counter; he reached for it without opening his eyes and brought it into his lap. The kitchen smelled of cilantro and eggs and burning ink.

I said, "Mrs. Martinez just hired me."

"You're white," the other waitress said. Her eyebrows were penciled on. Both of the women looked tired to me, fierce and old. She said, *"Ay dios mío.* Affirmative action at La Cocina."

The cook mumbled something no one understood. The flaming newspaper made me think of the downtown curio shops where old women rubbed oil on your palms to predict your future.

The cook said, "Am I being fired again?"

"Fired," the waitress said, eyeing the burning newspaper. "Now he's a comedian. Now he's Cheech and Chong."

"I'm the new delivery driver," I said. "My name's Julian. Everyone calls me Jay."

"Julian," the cook said. "Julian, what kind of car do you drive?"

"A Cadillac," I said. The waitresses glared at me. I saw that the one holding the menu was a lifetime younger than I'd originally thought. It occurred to me that she was the other woman's daughter. My father's tie suddenly felt tight around my neck. An hour earlier, he'd tied it on himself in the mirror, then loosened the knot and slipped it over my head. Now I wished I'd left it in the car. I said, "It's a convertible Fleetwood."

"The King of the Cadillac line," the cook said.

"Exactly."

"Julian, when I own this restaurant—"

"Ay dios mío," the older waitress said and took her tray of salsa cups out of the kitchen. Her daughter rolled her eyes and started fanning the smoke again. Her hair hung in thick spirals, her nails were glittery vermilion. She said, "Carlos, Jay's worked here for two minutes and already you're starting with your fantasies."

Carlos raised the beer to his lips and awkwardly tried to sip without disturbing the newspaper in his ear. I wanted to ask why it was there, but also wanted to act unfazed, like I encountered such things daily. When Carlos couldn't manage a drink, he extended his arm behind him and emptied the bottle into a pot of simmering menudo.

"Julian," he said, "when I buy this restaurant, you'll deliver tacos by limousine."

The Caddy was cream-colored, a 1978 Brougham. Whitewalls, chrome, power windows, locks, and mirrors, and leather seats and a retractable antenna. Even at thirteen years old, the Fleetwood wasn't a car my family could normally afford—my father drove a Datsun pickup, my mother a Chevy hatchback—but an old woman had pawned it, and when her loan expired, my father brought the keys home. Things had already soured in their marriage by then, but my mother had always coveted a convertible, and my father knew her boss drove one, so he must have hoped that a luxury sedan could turn things around for our family, deliver us to a different destiny.

He was the manager of Blue Water Pawn, and he believed everything you'd ever need would eventually float through the pawnshop doors. My mother's opal earrings and pearl necklace, her espresso machine and electric range and Tiffany lamps, my ten-speed bike and computer, my cordless phone and bowie knife and Nikon camera, all of it had once belonged to someone else, and either the owners or the people who'd robbed them had sold the stuff to Blue Water for pennies on the dollar. My father once paid twelve bucks for an acoustic guitar that had belonged to Elvis Presley, and he gave it to my mother for one of their anniversaries. I'd been forbidden from telling my friends about the guitar, but I regularly bragged about it. Sometimes I lifted it from its fur-lined case and strummed its strings.

That the Cadillac came through the pawnshop surprised everyone except my father, and for a while that surprise buoyed my parents. Every couple of weeks they soaped the car with sponges and waxed it until their reflections emerged in the hubcaps. They took it to open-air restaurants on the Laguna Madre, and on weekends they drove into the hill country with the top down. When they returned the seats were littered with pine needles and mesquite leaves, the floorboards dusted with sand like confectioner's sugar. Once, they stopped at a rest area outside Austin and had someone snap a photo of them with my Nikon. They're wearing sunglasses, leaning on the Fleetwood with the tawny hills rolling into the horizon behind them; the landscape looks like a solemn, arrested wave, and studying the picture closely, you can almost sense that my mother is poised to tighten her scarf around her hair and walk out of the frame for good.

On the second anniversary of the night she moved to Arizona with her boss, my father calmly walked outside and cut the Fleetwood's ragtop into ribbons with my bowie knife. When he came back in, he said, "Pop quiz."

Ever since I'd started high school he'd been quizzing me: Name the capital of Delaware. What was the shortest war in history? Who invented wallpaper? When I botched the answers—I'd never answered one correctly—he'd say, "Time to hit the books." My father had his GED.

I couldn't tell if he knew I'd watched him shred the vinyl, so I tried to act casual. I was also worried he'd ask me about my mother. She called me every other month, but sometimes my father answered before I could reach the phone. I hadn't heard from her in a while, so we were both anticipating her call.

I said, "Ready, professor."

"Tonight's prize is a 1978 Fleetwood Brougham, the King of the Cadillac line."

I didn't know what he'd done with my knife. Maybe he'd stabbed it into the steering wheel or one of the whitewalls. My father twirled the keys around his finger. He'd been trying to unload the car for two years.

He said, "What's the beginning of wisdom?"

I knew the answer immediately. A bronze plaque with the words engraved on it hung in his office at Blue Water. I said, "The beginning of wisdom is the acquisition of a roof."

"Touchdown," he said and chucked me the keys.

Later that night I walked by his bedroom and heard him crying. His door was closed, but his sobbing was hard enough to carry into the hall. His room wasn't the one he'd shared with my mother—he'd converted the master bedroom into a storage space and pushed his bed into our old study—though when I pictured him, I couldn't help imagining the furniture as it had been before she left. I saw my mother's vanity under the shuttered window, saw my father trying to muffle his weeping with one of her tasseled pillows.

"Jay," he said through the door. "Jay, are you out there?"

"Just returned from my maiden voyage, professor."

For a moment I thought he hadn't heard me, thought maybe I hadn't spoken at all. Then he said, "I left the paper on the counter."

I wondered if this was a new kind of quiz. I said, "Ready, professor."

"Roofs cost money. I'd say it's time you found gainful employment."

"Right away," I said. I thought he'd say something more, or that I would, maybe *I love you* or *Thank you* or *I'm sorry Mom hasn't come home,* but finally I just walked into the kitchen and read the classifieds. I called La Cocina because a delivery job would afford me more time in the Caddy.

When I'd worked at Blue Water, the man who stocked the Pepsi machine would brag about free lap dances when his route took him to The Landing Strip out by the airport, and a customer—a young guy who delivered newspapers and always pawned his fishing rod—said he'd twice happened upon a married couple having sex in their front yard, but most of my deliveries went to construction sites or businesses where women wore suits and bifocals: banks, other restaurants, a fabric store, a podiatrist's office. Mornings were our busiest time, and there was usually a lunch rush, but by mid-afternoon our phone stopped ringing and Mrs. Martinez tallied our receipts. I swept and watered the potted ivies and ferns behind the cash register.

At the end of my first week I asked Melinda—who *was* Alma's daughter and a year older than me—why we didn't stay open for dinner. She said, "The only ones that come after lunch are wearing suits."

She was wiping down the tables before I flipped the chairs and balanced them on the Formica. When Melinda leaned over to spray the surface, I saw a butterfly tattoo on the small of her back.

"Suits? You mean, businessmen?"

"*Health department* suits," she said. "If we fail another inspection, they'll chain the door."

Before I'd left with my last delivery, Carlos had been chasing a roach around the kitchen, swatting at it with a menu. The stove was gummy with caked-on lard, and I'd watched Alma drink from the milk jug before pouring a glass for a customer. I said, "I guess a flaming sports section in the cook's ear could be considered unsanitary."

"*Aire de oído.* Like an ear infection. The smoke draws it out," she said.

"I know. My father—"

"How do you afford that car?" she interrupted. She was scrubbing the seat of a booth, trying to remove dried enchilada sauce. There were no more chairs to upend, so I was just waiting, watching her butterfly. She said, "Carlos says you sell drugs, Mama thinks you have a trust fund. I haven't asked Mrs. Martinez because she's all pissed."

"How do *you* think I afford it, Melinda?"

She plopped herself into the booth and looked me up and down. I tried to puff out my chest, and hoped she wouldn't notice my ears, which I knew turned red when I got nervous. She sucked in her cheeks, pursed her lips, squinted. Alma rolled a bucket and mop into the kitchen.

Melinda said, "You sell Avon. No, you mug old ladies. No, you're a hot-rodder. You won it in a midnight drag race."

"Close," I said, trying to sound serious. I remembered what my father told our neighbor when he asked about our new riding lawnmower. "I won it in a poker game."

She laughed so loud that Mrs. Martinez poked her head out of the office and whipped off her glasses. "Melinda, have you started making the hot sauce?"

"*Ya mero,*" she said. After Mrs. Martinez closed her door, Melinda said, "So, drugs or trust fund?"

Why I answered her the way I did is still a mystery to me. The words surprised me as much they did Melinda. I said, "The car was my mother's. She died two years ago. I inherited it."

Melinda squinted at me again, studied me in a softer way than before. I was waiting for her to react—to accuse or curse me, or start laughing again—when Carlos began singing in the kitchen. It was a Spanish song I'd heard playing on his transistor radio earlier that morning. Melinda continued assessing me. I stared at my shoes, at the restaurant's chipped linoleum.

Sliding out of the booth, she said, "Losing that pink tie after your first day was a good call. You look more like yourself now."

"You just met me," I said.

"Does that matter?" she said.

"Maybe not."

"You're cute," she said. "Especially when your ears turn red."

I never repaired the roof on the Caddy, and after a month of delivering tacos, I'd forgotten my father had ruined it. Summer in

Corpus is glomming. Thick, viscous heat, and there's no rain unless a hurricane is churning in the Gulf, so I just left the top down. I enjoyed smelling the baking asphalt, the far-off briny bay. When I saw someone I knew, I saluted them from behind the wheel. Or I turned up the stereo and pretended not to recognize them.

In July, Mrs. Martinez catered a wedding in Portland, the little shrimping town across the ship channel. It took me two trips to deliver all the food—two hundred enchiladas, vats of beans and rice, and bags of flour tortillas that I had to stash in the trunk. (A bag had flown out of the backseat on my first trip. When the wind lifted it into the night, it looked like a jellyfish swimming in black, black water.) By the time we'd set up the buffet it was ten o'clock. I'd thought I might drive Melinda home, but she had to serve coffee to the guests. She said, "If you stay, you can ask me to dance."

"I don't know how to dance," I said.

"Then stay and you can ask me *not* to dance."

I spent the next hour pacing outside the reception hall, pretending I'd just married Melinda. I stole glances at her serving flan and leaning down to ask if people wanted decaf or regular, and the simple fact of her knowing my name amazed me. The prospect of meeting her after dessert sent my heart kicking. I wondered if she was a virgin, if she knew I was. I almost vomited into a pot of azaleas.

When I looked up, Mrs. Martinez was standing over me, telling me to drive back to Corpus and make sure Carlos had locked up. The last time he'd been in charge of closing, he'd polished off a fifth of tequila and pushed each of the refrigerators into the dining area. She said, "Next morning, what do I have? Rotten food and a cook in the hospital with a hernia."

"Can Melinda come with me?"

Mrs. Martinez touched my cheek. She said, "Sweet Jay. Melinda just left."

As I drove back, moonlight marbled the slatey sky, and the bay under the Harbor Bridge stretched out like an endless expanse of deep, rich soil. I imagined Melinda riding beside me, her long hair whipping around us. I heard her small laugh that always reminded me of a sparrow bouncing into flight. With the Caddy coasting along Ocean Drive, I could almost feel Melinda reaching for my hand across the smooth seats. I'd only kissed one girl at a homecoming party, and I'd been too nervous to enjoy it. Our teeth knocked and scraped together, and her mouth tasted of meatloaf and wine coolers; after a few minutes of kissing, she fell asleep and I tiptoed out of the room, feeling simultaneously relieved and despondent. I thought Melinda's mouth would taste of cinnamon. "Melinda," I said aloud. "My Mexican lover."

I thought nothing of the few fat drops of rain that pelted me, nothing of the first thunderclap or the shudder of pink lightning or the heavy, muscular-smelling air that precedes a storm. But within a mile, rain was bouncing off my dashboard and drenching the seats and pooling under the accelerator. The windshield wipers sprayed the water back into my eyes and face, and the Fleetwood fishtailed around corners. Out of dumb instinct, I flipped the switch to raise the roof. The hinges lurched and moaned, a low steel-on-steel grinding like a hurt animal, and eventually the jagged strips of wet, ruined vinyl slapped down against me. I was a mile from home, but with the blurring rain and the wind pushing water over my windshield, I could only inch forward. I had to pull over when I couldn't see the lanes. The ragtop draped over my shoulders, like I'd gotten stuck in an automatic carwash.

When I unlocked our front door, the phone was ringing. I'd heard it when I was hustling up the slippery driveway, but I'd figured it for the sound of traffic sloshing by. My father's antique grandfather clock—another boon from the pawnshop—was about to hit midnight. For a beat, I allowed myself to believe Melinda was calling, but I knew better. In two years, my mother had never grasped the time difference between Corpus and Phoenix.

When I picked up, I heard, "Julian. This is Carlos, the cook from La Cocina."

I hadn't even said hello. I'd almost fallen trying to answer before the phone woke my father, and I was shivering in my soaked clothes. A puddle formed around my shoes.

"Is everything okay, Carlos?" With the storm, I'd forgotten to check the door at the restaurant.

"I'm calling to say we've never had a better driver. When I own the restaurant, I'm going to give you..." His voice trailed off, and it sounded like he was knocking a bottle against his forehead, trying to jog the word he wanted. I thought he might say *promotion* or *raise*, but he said, "A trophy. When I own La Cocina, I'm going to give you the blue ribbon."

My teeth wouldn't stop chattering. I said, "Thank you."

"Julian," he said, "the true reason I'm calling is for a small favor."

A ride, I thought. Through the front window, I could see the Fleetwood parked by the curb. In the streetlamp's amber glow, with the rain streaming over its body, the car looked immaculate and reposed. The upholstery was getting ruined, and I was to blame, but seeing the car like that, I felt an inexplicable pride.

Carlos said, "What I need, what I really need, is for you to bring me an accordion."

"An accordion?"

"This is life or death. I truly need this instrument," he said. "I wonder if your mom or dad plays the accordion, Julian. Maybe they have a spare."

"We're not a very musical family," I said.

"Because here's my idea," he said, then took a long pull from his drink. "When I own the restaurant, we'll have girls posing by the door in Santa costumes. They'll wave in customers. Or maybe they'll be naked except for Santa hats, and they'll play carols on accordions."

"The health department might frown on that, Carlos."

He knocked the bottle against his head again, then drained it and dropped it in the trash. I heard him pop a top with a bottle opener. Sounding suddenly sober and grim, he said, "Julian, you're right. Even with pasties, we'd be in trouble."

"Unfortunately."

"You're an idea man, Julian. Manager material. When I'm the boss—"

The line went dead. I was about to call Carlos back when my father said, "How was the old girl tonight?"

I didn't know how long he'd been behind me. He was leaning against the sink, wearing pajama pants and no shirt. The scar where he'd had his gall bladder removed looked like a centipede on his stomach. I said, "That was Carlos, from work."

"The cook calls you at midnight?"

"He was drunk. He wants an accordion. I told him to check Blue Water."

My father wasn't listening. He was peering over my shoulder, seeing the Fleetwood in the rain. Wet tallow leaves were stuck to its hood like leaches. The tattered roof looked like a busted garbage bag.

Our air-conditioner cycled on. I crossed my arms over my chest, which only made me colder.

My father said, "Pop quiz."

"Ready, professor."

He fixed me with his eyes again, then averted them to the car. He said, "What happens when a yacht fills with water?"

The question seemed deceptively easy, so I considered each word individually. Yacht. Fills. Water. But I couldn't think of any answer beyond the obvious one. I said, "It sinks."

"Touchdown," he said. Then he left me alone, trembling.

Carlos had gone outside after the phone went dead; he thought lightning had struck the shopping center; the floor and walls had jolted, like an earthquake. But there'd been no more lightning, just gusts of wind that blew the rain sideways and sent shallow waves rippling over the dark parking lot. He was about to return to the restaurant when he saw the downed telephone pole, then after he shelved his hands over his eyes, he recognized the car smashed under it, heard its weak, droning horn, and saw the headlamps shining dimly through the darkness. The driver was a college student named Whitney Garrett, and if Carlos hadn't carried her to his truck and driven her to the ER, she might've died.

I'd taken the morning off to bucket out the Caddy's floorboards, but that afternoon Carlos recounted everything. He was frying flautas, dancing around the kitchen with his spatula and beer. He said, "Cook saves princess, earns handsome reward."

"How handsome?"

"Julian, by the looks of Mama Garrett, I won't need to borrow your accordion again."

"Carlos, I don't own an accordion."

He slid the flautas onto the plate, spooned on extra rice and beans, then rang the bell for Alma to take the order to her table.

Carlos said, "*Yet.* You don't own an accordion yet."

But the reward never came. Days, then weeks, passed after he saved Whitney Garrett, and still Carlos heard nothing. He called me every few nights to talk to me while he drank. He asked if I'd enroll with him in classes to become a rodeo clown, and another time he told me the story of catching himself in his trouser zipper and getting stitches. He said, "Julian, that's happened to me *twice*, so please be careful." He told me that as a boy he'd wanted to be a mariachi singer, that his father had owned a monkey that smoked cigarettes. He talked about how he'd spend his reward money—he planned to buy La Cocina as well as a shrimp boat and recording studio, to outfit Alma with a new wardrobe, to send Melinda to college. He asked if I could think of why Mrs. Garrett would promise to visit the restaurant, but hadn't.

"Maybe she's planning something really special," I said.

"If someone saved my daughter, I'd give them the keys to my house. I'd send thank-you cards every morning. I'd call every night and sing them to sleep."

"Why does Carlos always talk about buying the restaurant?" I asked Melinda. We were eating a late lunch and trying out one of his new recipes. When he brought out the plates—steak picado in a taco shell bowl—he'd said, *In my restaurant, this dish goes on the menu. The Melinda and Julian Special.*

Melinda dabbed her mouth with a napkin and stared out the window, thinking. Puddles of heat radiated on the sidewalk, the grass across the street was as dry and blond as hay. I felt lucky to be in the air-conditioning, eating food that tasted of beer. The phone rang, and Mrs. Martinez answered, then walked the order into the kitchen. This was my favorite time of the day to look at Melinda, when her lipstick had worn off and her ponytail was loose. I imagined her looking this way just after waking. I wanted to stay in that booth forever.

She said, "Because Carlos is an optimist, like you."

"Like me?"

"He's always jabbered about owning a restaurant. For years he played the lottery, before that it was bingo. Now he thinks this girl's mother will be his ticket. Carlos thinks money will fall in his lap if he just waits long enough."

"And me? What am I waiting for?"

She took a long drink of sweet tea, crunched an ice cube. She said, "Me."

Mrs. Martinez ambled across the restaurant and handed me a bag of taquitos. She said, "To Beechwood Nursery, on Padre Island. Vamos, before the causeway gets bumper to bumper."

After she'd left I stood and looked down at Melinda. I said, "If I wait long enough, will something happen?"

She took a bite and chewed slowly, staring at me and smirking. "Do you think Carlos will ever buy La Cocina?"

As often as he'd mentioned it, I'd never really considered that possibility, and realizing that I didn't have an answer puzzled me. I felt shamefully confident that he'd never hear from the Garretts again—a month had passed—but that alone didn't preclude him from owning a restaurant. I said, "I hope so."

"Me, too," she said. Then she winked at me. "Plus, if he gets his own place, he's naming it *Melinda's*."

I thought she was joking, but then it clicked. I said, "You're Carlos's daughter?"

"Stepdaughter," she said.

Then, before I could stop myself, I said, "Melinda, I lied about my mother. She's not dead. She left my father to live with a lawyer in Arizona."

She took another bite, and my palms went clammy. Mrs. Martinez started feeding her plants behind me, though I could feel her leering at us. The phone rang again. I knew I needed to leave before I got stuck with another delivery, but my feet were rooted, like I'd stepped in drying cement.

Finally, Melinda said, "So it all makes sense."

"What does?"

"Your father," she said. "He's another optimist."

Driving to the nursery, I thought about this, my father being an optimist. He threw horseshoes alone in our backyard and listened to Bach suites while tinkering at his workbench. He read books about surviving divorce, and maybe because a book advised it, he'd started writing in a diary that he hid in his nightstand. I'd read a few pages, but then guilt swamped me, and I returned the notebook to its hiding place. He'd lectured me on responsibility because I'd ignored the ragtop, and when I told him about Carlos saving Whitney Garrett, he said, "I hope she *wanted* to be saved."

Roundtrip, the delivery took me two hours because the causeway had clogged with civilians leaving the Naval Air Station after their shifts. By the time I made it back to La Cocina, the health inspector had come and gone. The restaurant was empty, the door locked. The CLOSED notice and our failed inspection were posted in the window like new, elaborate menus.

At home, my father was watching *General Hospital.* He sometimes watched soap operas before work, maybe because my mother had watched them. The shows always left him cross. When he saw me, he clicked off the television and asked if I'd been messing with Elvis's guitar again.

I *had* been in his closet, twice in the last week, but I hadn't played the guitar. I'd just wanted to see it. I'd started thinking that my father only kept it around to punish himself, and holding the case, I felt sorry for him, and furious; I wanted to cut the strings in half, bash the guitar against the concrete.

I said, "I lost my job today. The health department shut us down."

My father levered himself from his recliner, set the remote control beside the lamp. He said, "Maybe now you'll have time to work on the ragtop."

I nodded. I felt my ears going scarlet.

"So, have you been fooling with the guitar?"

"No," I said.

"It's a collector's item, Jay. I shouldn't have to remind you how much it's worth. When I gave it to your mother, she—"

"Professor," I interrupted, "have you seen my bowie knife?"

I drove by two and three times a day, testing the lock and pressing my forehead to the window. The restaurant was like a diorama, and the longer I was kept out, the more I wanted back in, the more I felt that I'd never worked there at all. I loitered in the parking lot, hoping Carlos or Melinda would happen by, but they never did, and nothing ever changed. The notice stayed on the door, the chairs waited to be lifted onto the tables. Through the windows I watched the leaves of Mrs. Martinez's plants wilt and fall to the floor. Eventually, a moving crew carted the booths and tables and refrigerators onto a flatbed trailer; two weeks later, a wig store opened in our space.

When the phone rang one evening, I expected to hear Carlos's slurred voice on the line, but my mother said, "Do you hate me as much as your father does?"

Outside, I could hear him tightening a bolt with his drill. I remembered watching him thrash the ragtop, hearing him cry in his bedroom. In his journal, he'd written, *I hope Jay never loves someone the way I love you.* I said, "He doesn't hate you."

"That's a surprise," she said. "Your father, he's a—"

"An optimist," I said. I liked saying that, liked how it made me think of Melinda.

"An optimist. That's sweet of you. You're a good egg, Jay," she said. "Do you know when I think about him most? Around an election, when everyone blabs about Democrats and Republicans. Remember? *Republican.*"

Every pawnshop has a code that it uses for pricing—a ten-letter word with no repeating characters—and Blue Water's was Republican. Each letter represents a numeral (R is 1, E is 2, all the way through 0), so pawnbrokers can openly discuss how much to buy or sell merchandise for without betraying anything to customers. My father had taught us the code years before, so when he said he'd paid I-N-N for the Caddy, I knew he'd bought it for seven hundred. I'd tried to explain the code to Carlos one afternoon, and he said, "Julian, you shouldn't discuss politics at work."

My mother said, "I loved hearing the pawnshop guys talk that way. It excited me, a language you didn't hear if you didn't speak it. I still size things up like that. I'll think, Do I want to pay A-L for a blouse? Is an espresso really worth B? Is R-N-N-N too much to send in my Jay's birthday card?"

"I never got a birthday card," I said.

She went quiet. I listened to the static crackling on the line, to my father putting away his tools in the garage. He'd been working out there for hours each evening, and I'd been dodging him.

My mother said, "Maybe my calling was a bad idea, maybe I'll let you go."

"I'm glad you called," I said.

"That's nice to hear," she said and started crying a little. Once she'd composed herself, she said, "So, the check's in the mail, as they say."

"Thank you."

"And Jay, when you get your money, treat your father to a fancy restaurant. Or, one night when he's not expecting it, bring him home a steak and asparagus. That's his favorite meal, and he'd like you showing up with it."

Outside, our automatic garage door started closing. The light on the driveway diminished, diminished, diminished, and I heard my father run water to rinse his hands with the garden hose.

I said, "I'll deliver it in a limo."

For the two years between my mother's leaving and my father giving me the Cadillac, he intentionally left the keys in the ignition and the doors unlocked. He said he wanted someone to steal the car so he could file an insurance claim. I'd believed him at the time, but after La Cocina closed, I found myself thinking more about it and doubting him. He'd never put an ad in the paper or a FOR SALE sign in the window, so I suspected that he wouldn't have reported the car stolen or tried to claim any money; I think he wanted the car gone, but couldn't bear to get rid of it. My father, I think, was an idealist.

I worked at Blue Water until school started up again. I loaned thieves and addicts money for mounted javelina heads and leather jackets and leaf blowers; I sold stolen pistols to cops and widows and preachers. I listened to men lie about women and fishing, brawling and hunting, and my father taught me how to study a diamond through a jeweler's lens, to see how its imperfections determined its beauty. He quizzed me on how much to pay for solitaires, how low to sell princess cuts. We spoke in code. We skirted the topic of the Fleetwood's roof. In September, the heat relented and troughs of cooler air brought bands of rain in from the Gulf. If I saw thunderclouds carpeting the sky through Blue Water's windows, I'd run into the parking lot and cover the Fleetwood's interior with a tarp. I weighted the corners with barbells someone had pawned, and after the rain dispersed, I wadded the tarp into a ball and shoved it in the trunk.

One Friday night—Blue Water's busiest because everyone needs loans for the weekend—I pulled out my tarp and uncovered a bag of tortillas from the wedding Mrs. Martinez had catered in Portland. The tortillas had slipped under the spare tire and were fuzzy with gray mold. My stomach went whispery, my ears burned. I wanted to throw the bag into the street or on top of the pawnshop's roof, but I left it where it was and slammed the trunk shut and drove home.

The phone was ringing when I got to the house, but I didn't answer it. My father had barged into Blue Water's parking lot as I was accelerating away, and I didn't want to hear how I'd disappointed him again. He called a second, third, and fourth time, but I only stared at the receiver, unable to will myself to answer. *He'll tell me I'm irresponsible,* I thought. *He'll say I lack discipline.* When I finally picked up, his voice was tight and deliberate. "Stay there," he said. "We need to break bread."

"Will do, professor."

Five minutes later he called back. I answered by saying, "Still here, professor."

"Julian? This is Carlos. Maybe you remember me. I used to work—"

"Where are you?" I asked. Then I was out the door.

They lived in a section of Corpus called The Cut, a neighborhood crowded with rusted, broken-down cars and dirt lawns and boxy tract houses. If the stop signs hadn't been stolen, they were spray-painted with looping gang tags. White-shirted men anchored street corners; women sat on porches and rocked crying babies. A German shepherd lunged against a chain-link fence as the Caddy crawled by, and the air was tinged with mesquite smoke, someone barbecuing or burning branches. A young girl was pinning wet sheets to a clothesline. The streetlights were flickering to life when I saw her, and in the darkness, it looked like she was raising long flags of surrender.

Carlos was doing figure-eights on a BMX bike in the middle of his street. He looked like a child learning to ride without training wheels. When he saw me, he laid the bike on the curb and sauntered to the Fleetwood. He'd holstered a beer bottle in each of his front pockets, and he gave one to me. We leaned against my rear bumper, watching the night sky thicken.

"A toast," he said. We raised our bottles. "To La Cocina. May she rest in peace."

He'd been working day labor, taking the bus across town each morning and waiting outside Home Depot until someone hired him to clear brush or build a fence or fix a toilet. Melinda had started school again, and Alma was cleaning houses. No one had heard from Mrs. Martinez. That day, Carlos had helped a crew dig up a Country Club yard and install a sprinkler system; he'd worked for fourteen hours, then called me when he came home. He finished his beer and lobbed it at a trashcan, missing by a foot. He held his arm in the air like a basketball player after a jump-shot, and I smelled his sweat. The odor wasn't foul, just that of a body after a day's work. It smelled vaguely of La Cocina, of the last summer.

"A wig store moved into our old space," I said. "It's kind of sad, I guess."

He nodded twice, shoved his hands in his pockets, and stared into the darkness. I guessed he'd visited the restaurant, too, and was remembering the old days, but he said, "If I owned a wig store, I'd have full-bodied mannequins instead of the little heads. I'd leave them naked except for the wigs. That way, when there were no customers, I'd have something to look at besides hair."

"No health code violations in that," I said.

Down the street a man pushing a rickety snowcone cart argued with a teenager. The teenager whistled a hard, sharp whistle, and the man trundled away. I took a drink of my beer and tried to think of a way to ask if Melinda was home.

"Julian, driving the King of the Cadillacs out here was maybe not your best idea," Carlos said. "Two weeks ago, they shot a deaf guy because they thought he was making gang signs with his hands."

I'd heard the story at Blue Water. After the shooting, my father took each of his pawnbrokers aside and told them to be vigilant about background checks before selling guns. But standing with Carlos, I wasn't scared, and I hadn't been afraid navigating the streets. The world seemed random and unknowable to me, but not utterly cruel, not terrifying. Sometimes circumstances put you face to face with people you never thought you'd see again, and with that possibility in mind, you could make a life.

"Pop quiz," I said to Carlos. I'd turned around and was unlocking the trunk. I said, "Why did I rush over here tonight?"

"Julian, if I owe you any money—"

"You don't," I said. "Guess who I ran into."

I took my tarp out of the trunk. I'd handed Carlos my beer, and when I looked up at him, he was scratching his head with it. He said, "Julian, I'm not so good at tests."

"Mrs. Garrett. Whitney Garrett's mother," I said. "She came to La Cocina trying to find you. I was up there, looking in the window."

Carlos swigged from my beer, then swallowed hard and swigged again. He said, "Julian, are you fucking with Carlos?"

"She wanted to thank you for saving her daughter. She wanted to give you your reward," I said. I lifted the case from my trunk and clicked open the latches. In the violet moonlight, the strings shone like spun silk. The fur-lined case looked like a jewelry box.

I said, "For you, Carlos."

"A guitar," he said.

"It used to belong to Elvis Presley," I said. "It's worth—"

"She must have known I love music. Maybe I said something at the hospital."

"Probably," I said. "You were probably trying to take her mind off the accident."

"Carlos knows how to comfort the ladies." He admired the guitar at arm's length, then held it close and strummed an open chord, then another and another. When the notes died away, I suggested he sell the guitar and put the money toward starting his own restaurant. He said, "Julian, I'll never sell this."

"Where are we going?" Melinda said from behind us.

She'd climbed over the door and into the driver's seat of the Fleetwood. Behind the wheel, she looked exhausted and beautiful, just as she had on the day she'd told me Carlos was her stepfather.

"Field trip in the Fleetwood!" Carlos sang.

He jogged around the front of the car, strumming his strings. He set the guitar on the backseat first, then lowered himself in beside it. I sat in the passenger seat. I must have ridden that way when my mother owned the car, but I couldn't recall ever sitting there before. With the night sky starless and heavy above us, those days seemed part of another boy's life. I didn't know what to say, and had I spoken, I wouldn't have recognized my own voice.

Melinda fixed me with her eyes. I thought she was waiting for me to pass her the keys, but even after I did, she kept looking at me.

"Hey, you," she finally whispered. Then she winked and cranked the ignition.

She hung a U-turn and wound her way out of The Cut. She headed straight for the freeway and floored the gas once she hit those clean wide-open lanes. She took the car to speeds I never would, the speedometer needle trembling toward eighty, eighty-five, ninety. The streetlamps whizzed by like comets. Carlos was strumming and singing in the backseat, but I could barely hear him over the engine and the air whooshing around the windshield. Melinda's hair swirled wildly, and the scent of her honeyed shampoo wafted. It seemed we were floating.

I'm not sure when I realized she was driving to La Cocina, or when I realized she didn't know the restaurant was gone. Maybe I knew it when she exited the freeway doing sixty and it felt slow as walking. Maybe it was when she braked at an intersection and the speed had left her giddy enough that she leaned over and kissed me so hard and long that drivers behind us laid into their horns. Maybe it was when I looked back, worrying Carlos would be angry, and found him fast asleep, cradling the guitar. Or maybe I realized it when the night sky opened and the rain poured. Before I could stop her, Melinda flipped the switch to raise the roof. I thought of how disappointed my father had been by my neglecting the ragtop and how I'd been avoiding him because it shamed me, too. With the rain drumming on the hood and streaking the glass, I thought of him finding the house empty tonight. I'd never disobeyed him like that before, but now I thought he'd forgive what I'd done, maybe even approve of it. As a new pristine ragtop eased down and the rain grew quieter and quieter, I saw my father working those many nights in his garage: He's stretching the vinyl taut over the roof's ribs, riveting the corners, oiling the hinges. He's listening to the intricate music of longing and weeping when he must. He's watching the clouds. He's waiting and waiting, wiling away the hours until a storm gathers and his son can appreciate the painstaking labor of hope, the coded, sheltering lessons of sorrow.

ELLEN LITMAN

The Trajectory of Frying Pans

She was in her early twenties, five or six years younger than me. She moved with a catlike suppleness through our dull office space (scratchy fabric of cubicle walls, coiled wires, the kitchen with its empty Pepsi cans assembled into a shaky pyramid for future recycling). She wore skirts—nobody in our office wore skirts—short, flared skirts, narrow, stretchy ones, knee-length with flowers that made you think of summer. In the kitchen, the guys nudged me. What a chick, they said. You Russians with your Russian chicks. Too bad she's married, right? Too bad for you, buddy.

They hired her in September, after Labor Day. The reason I remember is I always remember a long weekend, and also because on Labor Day I had gone to a barbecue party to meet a certain Alla Mayskaya from Kiev. It rained, the barbecue had soaked through the plastic tent, and Alla Mayskaya never showed up. Returning home, hungry and mad, I thought how this was the last decent holiday until Thanksgiving, and how the following week at the office would be listless and long—computer screens oscillating softly, the management conspicuously absent, my coworkers stumbling along with their coffee, exchanging sleepy recollections of their own barbecues.

But the following week at the office was not like that.

Her name was Nadya Shipilova, though having recently married an American, she was now changing it to Nadya Briggs, which kept causing problems at the payroll department and in our internal e-mail system. They had put her in a cubicle by the window, next row from mine, and I could hear her phone conversations.

She made me remember Polina. They shared that awkward, long-limbed grace, except that Nadya's had a tinge of glamour, while Polina was a Turgenev girl (Asya or Jemma, *First Love* and *Spring Torrents*), leaning against a birch, hiding a book behind her back as I snapped pictures of her in Sokolniki Park.

I ran into Nadya in the mailroom two days after she first showed up at the office. It was a Thursday. I never got mail at the office, but by Thursday you needed diversions—you drove from lunch the long way, you waited for the slow elevator, you made side trips to check out office supplies.

Nadya was trying to send a fax. She looked up when I came in, and I said hello.

"You know how this works?"

I said I didn't know but could try to figure it out. I regretted it immediately. I could have hidden behind a laconic *sure* or *nope*, but the long sentence gave me away.

"You're from Russia, no?"

I said yes, I was Mike, or Misha, or whatever; it really didn't matter after all these years, though here at work, *Mike* was probably more appropriate.

"I'm Nadya," she interrupted me.

"I know," I said, stupidly.

We both looked down at the fax machine, the scattering of cover sheets around it. I asked her where she'd gone to school.

She told me Allegheny College, Meadville. Before that? MGU—Moscow State University. She shrugged a little. "Where everybody went, I guess."

She guessed wrong. I punched a button that said RESET, and the fax machine began its even warbling. Some people went to MGU, and others went to the Institute of Petrochemical Engineering (also known as the Kerosene Institute). Some, with resounding Russian last names (ending in -*eva* and -*ova*), were sent on exchange programs to small liberal colleges in America, and others, like myself, with decidedly un-Russian swarthiness, dropped out after the first semester, sold furniture and books, and stood in line at the Department of Visas and Permits. To our coworkers, Nadya and I were equally Russian. They didn't know the difference, but I knew.

Before leaving the mailroom, I remembered how to work the fax machine: press 1 and then 9 to dial an outside number. I told this to Nadya in English. Then I threw in a terse *Take care*, one of those colloquial things that implied, *We are colleagues, you mean nothing to me.* If I said it quickly, it almost completely concealed my accent.

Two things happened the summer before: I got a letter from Polina, the first one after seven years; and I began dating again.

The dates were mostly blind dates, or half blind, as I called them whenever a relative or a coworker produced a picture in advance. I approached them systematically, developed a list of favorable locations—uncrowded restaurants with outdoor patios, small cafés with flickering candles and a New Age slant, museum rooms filled with pensive quietness and hollow footsteps.

I went out with Mila, the nicer of the twin sisters from Donetsk, and with Tanya Katz, who was studying to be a doctor. I took Zoyka Kamyshinskiy to the symphony. Sveta Metsler, a graduate student in Slavic Languages, invited me over for dinner. The results were disappointing. Mila worked as a realtor (she'd never finished college); Tanya Katz was separated (her husband, Petya, worked at my company); and Alla Mayskaya, when I finally met her, shortly after Labor Day, showed up with a small gold cross around her neck. The cross was what got me. I told my mother we didn't immigrate so I could date a chauvinist from Kiev.

When I didn't have dates, I stayed in my apartment, a top-floor studio on Forbes, above the Squirrel Hill Fitness Center for Women. It was a simple place: a futon always unfolded, three bookshelves, a TV sitting on a chair. At night, I microwaved the soup my mother dispatched to me in flimsy plastic containers. There was very little to do. I could read *The Wall Street Journal*. I could think of applying to business schools, of moving away. From my window I could watch women in T-shirts and tight pants sweep in and out of the fitness center all evening long. Or else I could reread Polina's letter.

We had met in high school and fell in love around graduation exams. My memories were like blurred strips of a documentary: May, turbid air, drizzling rain. Polina in a loose red trench coat, stepping over puddles in her delicate shoes. Her face, upturned and lovely, somehow lightened by the rain, like poetry, wild and strange. There was a kind of reverence between us—that's what I remembered best—the love of a higher order or some other nonsense we believed in back then. A year later I left for America, and Polina stayed.

In the letter, she wrote that she had gotten married, happily, to an old college classmate, whom I'd never met. *Are* you *with somebody? You don't have to tell me,* she said. She hoped I, too, had found happiness. She hoped that I'd write her back and that we could be friends—*The past is behind us now*—though she admitted she'd never told her husband about me.

I had been listening to Nadya all morning; I couldn't help it; her voice, her laughter, her throaty interjections scattered through the office in droplets, bright and girlish. What she said wasn't important. She was full of cheap American cheer: there was a furniture sale at Kaufmann's, dance lessons in Squirrel Hill, a black tabby cat at the Bethel Park Petco. Just before lunch, I heard her on the phone with her husband, Dan—she called him *Danechka*—plodding through mushy Russian endearments, enunciating them. *Danechka* was learning Russian.

She stopped by after lunch, stood leaning against the side of my cubicle, one knee half bent below the flounce of her skirt, her shoe—its sole thick, with deep grooves—powerful and clumsy like a small tank. She said she was writing a loading script and wanted to ask me some questions about the database and the product. I said okay and nodded for her to sit on the extra— "guest"—chair. She did so gracefully, crossing her legs and arranging her skirt in waves of Mediterranean blue.

She said, "I saw you last night. You were with a girl, near the university."

I coughed. "An acquaintance from school."

It was like making bad excuses: everything I said came out clipped and unconvincing.

She smiled, and then produced her list of work-related questions. I had trained new employees before, and now I was prepared to unfurl for her my lecture. But Nadya was quick—I didn't expect her to be so quick. She asked me the right sorts of questions, specific and probing. If I lingered on something she'd already learned, she would chime in to let me know.

The girl she had seen me with was a blind date, Alina, dark-haired and pretty, with narrow shoulders and a delicate, knifelike profile. Her voice was full of raspy Ukrainian consonants, but I could learn to like those. She was an undergraduate, studying nutrition, and we had agreed to meet by Hillman Library on campus. It was five o'clock, and the food trucks, usually sprawled along the curb, were packing up, ready to leave. I suggested a Middle Eastern restaurant on North Craig. Alina's eyes slid over me, dark and noncommittal. She was appraising me: one point for my tallness, another for my sweater (which revealed my good taste and good money), minus two points for my glasses and bookishness.

There was a bar, she said. She'd seen its happy hour advertised in the *Pitt News*. Besides, she had a class at seven-thirty.

I took her to the bar, a sweaty room packed with broad-faced undergraduates in laundered baseball hats turned backwards. We had to press against them as we made our way into a corner vacant enough for standing. I bought her a beer and got myself a glass of water—another point subtracted. I asked her if she liked her major. She said it was okay and looked past me, flashing a beguiling smile at someone at the other end of the bar.

Nadya sighed and shifted in her chair. Somehow we had gotten through all the work-related questions, and now, inexplicably, I was telling her about my date. She listened, sympathetic, engaged, but also amused. "You need a serious girl," she said. Her eyes, liquid amber, were flecked with quick humor.

I was glad I could amuse her. The rest of my coworkers missed my humor. Women spoke to me with practiced clarity. Men performed their careful jokes. *How you doing, Mike?* they said. *How's life?* Life was shooting upward like a fountain, like a wrench hitting you in the face. When I spoke, their faces took on a strained, concerned expression, as if I were someone with special needs.

After work, I drove to my mother's. She lived in a two-bedroom apartment on Hobart. She'd never learned to drive, and though the nearest supermarket was only a few blocks away, I took her grocery shopping every week. The walk from my apartment to her place took seven minutes—I had timed it one day.

I found her in the living room, standing on a stepladder, with a hammer in her hand and two nails gripped between her teeth.

"What on earth are you doing up there?" I said.

She was with her best friend, Tamara, an older woman with plucked eyebrows, who came over nearly every day to lecture my hapless mother.

"I brought your mother a painting," said Tamara. She sat in my mother's armchair, her shoes off, her legs thick in opaque medical stockings. I was supposed to call her *Aunt Tamara*.

I turned to my mother again. "For God's sake, take that rust out of your mouth."

She shook her head, and her black curls flopped and her big-framed glasses slid down to the tip of her nose. She was like a girl on top of that ladder, in the white turtleneck and black slacks she wore to her accounting job downtown. She spat out the nails and told me she was done. The painting was balanced on a precarious hook she'd just hammered in.

"Is it crooked?" she asked.

"It's fine," I said. It was a pond, a sunset.

I helped her down the stepladder, and she kissed me on the forehead.

"How was your day?" she said.

"A normal day."

"Have you accomplished everything you wanted to accomplish?"

This was what she used to ask my father. The same tone, too, anxious to please and prying and also, somehow, patronizing. My father left before I entered high school. Their marriage had been a disaster, a string of loud, loveless fights, his temper flaring, the noise of broken furniture, the shards of ruined glasses.

She said, "I got you something." Her voice turned small. "A phone number. Tamara's niece."

She handed me a scrap of paper. It had a number with an unfamiliar area code, and underneath there was a name, Lariska.

"From New York," said Tamara.

My mother winked at her, and she responded by rounding her mouth into a lipsticked O of mock excitement. They waited for me to react.

"He's being shy," said Tamara.

"He's being coquettish," said my mother. "He's flirting without honey cakes."

I cringed, and my mother said, "You know I don't like it when you make that face."

They wanted some other reaction, enthusiasm or gushing gratitude. I remembered Lariska. She was plump, loudmouthed. I remembered she had slept around a lot.

"I thought you wanted this," my mother said, at once apologizing and accusing.

I had told her I wanted the dates. But when she hassled me and fussed and brought me these scraps of phone numbers, I felt smothered, a pitiful mess of a person. It was like being sick: nostrils itching, head filled with cement, and here's Mother, spooning the medicine, fixing the sheets, reminding: *There's no one else to take care of you.*

She had been watching my expression. "Why do you hate me so much?" she said. Her voice slipped into a whisper, her lips twitched, and I thought she might cry. But she stopped herself—for Tamara—and her lips, now tight with control, contorted into a smile.

"Look at this painting," she said. "So pretty. Thank you, *Aunt Tamara.*"

Tamara bugged her eyes at me, but I ignored her. This was my mother's shtick, and we both knew how to play it. We played it well. I went up to my mother and hugged her. She tucked her chin against my shoulder.

"You're sure it's not crooked," she said, "the painting?"

"It's perfect," I said.

The next week, I ran into Nadya at our cafeteria downstairs. We waited in line together. She was getting an egg salad sandwich if it didn't have chopped celery, or a turkey sandwich if it did. I was getting chicken, which came with yellow rice, so cold and hard it was like swallowing small pebbles.

"I saw you again," said Nadya. "With a girl, near Carnegie Museum."

We had brought our trays to a small table in the corner.

"A different girl," she said.

"Ughu." With my mouth full, I made a sound like an eagle owl, which made her chuckle. "Affirmative."

"Another acquaintance?"

I shook my head. "A date."

"You must think I'm spying on you." Nadya leaned in, and her earrings dangled toward me and caught the light.

"That's right," I said. "That's what I think."

"Well, I'm not." She pulled away and straightened her back primly. "We live around there, Dan and I. Across from the museum. You know the apartment building? With a flower van always parked outside?"

I said I knew the van.

"But we're buying a house soon. So no more spying." She puffed up her lips in a flirtatious, sulky way.

"I'm counting on that."

I knew about the house and about Dan. He drove her to work every morning and picked her up at the end of each day. I'd met him once. He was young but shriveled, full of adolescent intensity, with a Ph.D. in computer science from Carnegie Mellon. The guys at the office had seen him, too. They wanted to know why a pretty Russian girl like Nadya had to go and marry such a nerd. Those poor girls, my mother said, they understand what's good for them. Nobody wants to go back to Russia.

But Nadya's happiness was so convincing. I saw her in the morning getting out of Dan's car, quickly daubing her nose with powder, kissing Dan on the cheek, chirping something abrupt and sweet in his ear. And then she was walking toward the entrance, gathering her hair in a clip, clutching her small handbag full of to-do lists and important phone numbers, her face slack and distracted, a schoolgirl in love.

Nadya and I had finished our food but remained at the lunch table, slouched over the empty plates, our conversation clicking along like a plastic ball on a ping-pong table.

"Tell me about your date," said Nadya.

I told her this was an experiment—I was experimenting with dating. I told her about Polina's letter, and it nearly broke Nadya's heart.

"Are you sure you're ready?" she asked me. "For dating?"

"It's been seven years. I better be ready."

Was I melodramatic? I probably was. Half the time I believed in my grief for Polina. In a movie theater, for example, when the music welled up at the closing credits. In the fall, when the leaves whispered sadly and got caught in the brown hair of passing university girls.

"It was nobody's fault," I explained, making vague, expansive gestures. It was nice to pretend that Polina and I had been fated lovers, separated by distance, by sickness, by curse—the film version of *Great Expectations*. I described our feelings as refined and exalted, which was true and which had gotten us in trouble in the first place.

I didn't tell Nadya the truth.

Polina had wanted to come to America. To follow me, she explained, as if America were Siberia, and she, Polina, a Decembrist's wife or Raskolnikov's Sonya. I told her it wouldn't work.

The last time I saw her, back in Moscow, she came to me unexpectedly, simply showed up one evening and rang the doorbell. My mother let her in. We were scheduled to leave in two months, and the whole apartment was in turmoil, books on the floor, furniture dismantled, my mother on the phone, in tears, battling with my father over the goddamn apartment. To sell or not to sell. And then Polina stepped into my room. Unnatural, unreal. She had that sickly look, her face drawn and pale, like she was suffering. I turned away. Outside it was snowing, and I stood with my face against the windowpane and watched the spiraling of snowflakes, so slow and peaceful I could slip into unconsciousness. "Look at me," said Polina. "Why won't you look at me?"

The love boat crushed against everyday drudgery, wrote Mayakovsky in his suicide note, and I was no Mayakovsky and never owned a revolver. What I told Nadya was this: You love somebody, or you think you love somebody, so you marry (if you're in Russia), or don't marry (if you're in America), but either way, you begin living together—small apartment, closed space, overflowing closets—and maybe for a while you're happy. But then, a month later or maybe two, you start to notice things— unswept bread crumbs, wet swirls of hair in the drain, the way she asks you questions at the movies, as if you've seen the film already. And after three months? You're fighting all the time, about money, laundry, spotty hygiene. Your rooms are small, you're pinched against each other. And it only gets worse after that, so after six months, you measure the trajectory of frying pans as she hurls them at you from the kitchen.

I stopped talking. The lunch hour was over, and everyone had left. We sat alone in the unburdened cafeteria.

"That's not how it works," said Nadya.

There was something reproachful in her voice, something frosty and proper. Then it hit me: she was getting defensive. And for the first time I thought that maybe her own marriage wasn't all that solid. It pleased me for a moment, and then I felt bad for her.

"You're right. I don't know how it works," I said. "I've never really lived with anybody."

And then it was October, and I was trying to date Sveta Metsler from Slavic Languages. We had met back in August but only gone out four times, due to Sveta's torturous suspicions. I called her to make dates, and later she called me to cancel them, because, she explained, I didn't *really* like her. She had a turned-up nose and light chubbiness, which I thought was sweet and earthy. But she hated it. She was angry at herself for her chubbiness, she was angry at Slavic Languages for being such a perfect yet impractical pursuit, and she was angry at America for anything she couldn't blame on Slavic Languages.

"Why are they so angry," I asked Nadya, "these girls I meet?"

"Maybe they all have a cold." She sniffled and pulled another tissue from a box on her desk. Nadya was fighting a cold.

I had brought her both DayQuil and NyQuil. "It's easy," I said. "You take one in the morning and one before bed, and everything assumes its rightful place."

"I can't," she said. "My heart starts pounding. I'm probably allergic." She sniffled again and blew her nose. "But tell me about your date."

Tell me about your date, she kept saying week after week. She avoided calling them by their names, perhaps out of forgetfulness, or maybe—I hoped—to point out their insignificance. The dates came and went, but Nadya was always there, in her cubicle decorated with family photographs and candy-colored greeting cards. We often worked together in that cubicle, twining a jagged line of code and jostling over her keyboard—a break of laughter, a friendly brawl. At noon we drove to lunch. When we returned, our office smokers, assembled outside, winked at us through their hazy cigarette clouds. Did Nadya notice how they winked?

Tell me about your dates, she said, and I told her as best as I could. They were nice Russian girls, my dates; they wore sexy button-down shirts, and their eyes were tastefully underlined in black. The moment I saw them I was smitten; I could forgive them anything in that first moment. But then we spoke, they spoke—recounting the years in America and the respective places of origin—and soon the conversations tapered off, revealing my

high-mindedness, or their indifference, or something else, something small and shallow within us. And then we talked about the
weather, our glances sailing past each other.

I tried to explain this to Nadya, and she groaned a little, like she
thought I was one of those guys who never knew what they wanted and never wanted what they had.

"Okay," I said. "Maybe *I'm* the boring one. What do I know?
Computers? Stock market?"

"You're not boring," said Nadya.

"Should I talk to them about the weather?"

She looked at me, quietly, sadly.

"That might be all right for starters," she said, "the weather."

At least, I thought, with Sveta Metsler I could talk about literature. But that was not what Sveta Metsler had in mind. She said
she had to sleep with me: she was twenty-five and had never done
it; that was the source of all her problems. We'd had dinner, pasta
and shrimp with inexpensive red wine, which burned bitterly
inside my throat, and later Sveta Metsler sat on the couch next to
me and played with the top button on her blouse.

I didn't sleep with Sveta Metsler. Instead we kissed and cuddled
and talked of figure skating and the stock market. She didn't want
to talk about literature at all. She'd taken off her blouse grudging-
ly, as if I'd asked her to, and revealed her soft white baby-flesh
with the red half-circles where the rims of her bra gripped her
harshly.

That night, on the way home, I drove by the apartment building with the flower van downstairs. I paused on the other side of
the street and looked at the windows, shaded and lit, unfamiliar
silhouettes caught in their domestic dance. Which one of them
was Nadya? A bus behind me honked—I was blocking its stop—
and I slowly drove away. Even if Nadya came out at that moment,
what could I tell her? What could I offer? She was up there, per-
forming her courageous acts of love—fake love, green card love—
and in the morning she would be at work, cheerful and
breathless, hurrying to a meeting, gasping, exhaling her *okh*s and
*akh*s, and later still she would be on the phone with Dan, calling
him sweet Russian names he didn't deserve, persuading him every
second that what they had was real, persuading all of us, persuading herself.

I called Sveta Metsler from work. I gave her the predictable excuses: She deserved something better. We were wrong for each other. It wasn't exactly untrue—there was some sense of honor involved in our negotiations—but mostly I was afraid that the reluctant compromise she had suggested would turn into routine.

"You should've given it a chance," said Nadya.

"Three months of living in the same apartment—"

She said, "The frying pans. I know."

I said we were all animals deep down. You had to really love each other before committing to the near-suicidal act of sharing your life.

"It doesn't have to be like that," said Nadya.

My blind dates slowed down. I began having dreams about Polina again, but it was a different Polina, pliant and approachable, warmed up and softened by Nadya's sexiness. She came into my room, and I wanted to tell her that I was sorry, but she laughed at me, the silver murmur, like it didn't matter anymore. Tell me about your dates, she said, and I woke up confused and desolate, and went to the kitchen to boil water for my morning tea.

At work every morning I waited for Nadya, but she was now often late. Her face was a little puffy, as if she had overslept or had been crying. She didn't look unhappy, but I noticed things. She was on the phone a lot, but she kept it quiet. Sometimes she took her calls in the conference room. Sometimes when I stopped by her cubicle at lunch, she was still on the phone. She gave me a five-dollar bill and covered the receiver with one hand. She said: Would you be a sweetheart and get me something? A sandwich, you know? I said I knew. An egg salad sandwich if it didn't have chopped celery.

She and Dan had moved into their house, and Nadya's commute was difficult. Dan couldn't drive her anymore; she had to take two buses each way. She tried to be content about that, but to me she admitted the truth: she was tired. She was starting to look sloppy, too, her hair tied in the back, her face makeup-less and raw. Instead of skirts, she wore overalls.

I had listened to her conversations with Dan, and I knew that they were banal and thick with sugary sentiments, that in the end they lacked the tender, flirtatious energy of our talks.

"Why can't he teach you to drive?" I said.

She rubbed her eyes. "I don't know. I've asked him before."

"You want me to teach you?"

She said, "That's sweet of you, but what's the point? Dan doesn't want to buy another car."

She coughed a little, and I thought, *Here we go, not another cold.* It was because of those buses, it was too much for her. She looked weakened, feverish that morning. I thought of taking the rest of the day off and driving her home. I had an image of her wrapped in blankets, her hair tousled, an old-fashioned thermometer sticking out from under her arm. I would stay with her until Dan came from work.

I said it was a crummy situation, I was worried for her.

"Sometimes you have to compromise," said Nadya.

"What if it's wrong? What if you compromise and later, say, a year later, you meet the one person you could love?"

I hadn't planned to say it, but once it was out I didn't want to stop. She looked at me, her face blurred with surprise and defeat and maybe—could it be?—hope. I wanted her to understand exactly what I meant, so I said, "Somebody you can talk to. The way we talk."

She said, "I'm pregnant." She waited a minute, to make sure *I* understood, and then something snapped in her. She turned away, slumped over her desk. I didn't know what to say to her. I stroked her shoulder and her back, feeling the corduroy strap of her overalls, the thinness of her blouse underneath.

They let us leave early that day. I drove Nadya home, a long, slow drive, stop-and-go in the traffic. She leaned her head against the passenger-side window, and we didn't talk the whole time. It worried me that we suddenly had nothing to say to each other.

Then we arrived. Nadya's pale yellow house looked pinned to the ground, scrunched under the flat, ample roof. It had one floor. Thick bushes, sculpted like urns, grew by the front door. A large stretch of short, withered grass sloped toward the road. There was no one around. No sidewalks or stores. We stayed in the car for a while.

"That's where you live?" I confirmed.

Nadya shrugged. "You want to come in? It's nicer inside."

I thought of Dan returning home. "Perhaps some other time."

She nodded quickly, as if to say she was sorry she'd asked. She placed one hand on the passenger-door knob and turned to thank me for the ride. It felt like I had just rejected her. I asked her to wait, and she did. A beautiful, excruciating minute—or ten, or fifteen. We were alone and quiet, some unseen threads drawn between us—restraint, attraction, doubt. Then I did something crazy: I leaned in and kissed her on the side of her mouth. "I'm so confused," whispered Nadya.

She said we had to talk, to discuss this, and though I wanted to talk right away, we agreed I'd come back on Sunday, when Dan would be out of town. I thought of Nadya as I drove home that night, and then inside my apartment, as I watched TV and ate soup cooked by my mother; and later when I turned the TV off I couldn't remember what I had just watched. I surveyed my apartment and imagined her there, looking at my books, sitting on the edge of my futon. This was all I could think of: the smell of her apple shampoo and how her knitted blouse felt slightly damp on her back when I touched her.

On Sunday I was back at Nadya's house. I knocked, and she opened the door. She'd been cleaning. I could tell it had been a productive morning for her. She wore jeans and an open-necked shirt, pink, scattered with small green flowers. I sat on the couch. The room wasn't at all like I'd imagined it. It looked chintzy, mismatched, with photographs pinned to the walls and fake plastic flowers. Nadya was poking around with a bottle of cleaning solution and a roll of paper towels. She was picking up things—Dan's things, I assumed—a pair of sneakers, a notebook. She said Dan had left in a hurry, a funeral in Harrisburg, a relative he hardly knew.

In my twenty-eight years I'd been to a funeral once. I guess you could say I was lucky, but the truth was I never knew most of my relatives. My parents were feuding, and this had divided our family. I wouldn't call it luck. It had been my grandmother's funeral, my father's side. I went with my mother; we took a bus to Vostryakovo Cemetery. It took us a while to find it, the plot and the funeral crowd. We got lost in back alleys, circuitous and muddy. Our shoes became covered in mud. We stood in the back. People looked at us strangely; they knew who we were, but no one talked to us.

Why did I think of it now? I was here, with Nadya, except she kept moving around. I couldn't quite focus on her. I thought what an awful house it was. The walls had a bleak, creamy color. The furniture smelled clammy and old. And Nadya was saying, *Dan, Dan, Dan.* Dan was sloppy; he left things behind him; she kept finding these horrible things: dried-up tea bags and calloused pizza slices. What's more, Dan was just like his father, whom they had seen in Philadelphia last month. "Two boots make a pair," said Nadya.

And now, I suddenly remembered my father's crystal shot glass, shaped like a boot. My father used to come home from work around eight, and we had supper in the kitchen. I was a fickle eater, which made my father mad. Most nights I was given a plate of buckwheat kasha with milk, and I splashed in it aimlessly. The wall where I sat was warm from the heating pipes inside it, and I liked to touch it with both of my hands. My father would tell me to behave myself. He'd look at my kasha, and his face would go puckered. "Take it away," he'd say to my mother, and she'd take my plate away. "Who are you taking after?" he'd say to me, which meant I was done, I could run into the next room and watch the children's evening program on TV, which started at eight-thirty. Except sometimes I stayed and listened to my father's stories about his coworkers with funny nicknames, the Prince, the Big-Eared, the Eagle Man.

Nadya stopped cleaning and sat next to me on the couch. She was suddenly tired, she said. It happened all the time now. She leaned back on the cushions. Her eyelids were daubed blue, and I knew she had done it on purpose, for me. But it didn't look good; it looked pathetic. And it made me feel sad, the thought of her getting ready for me like that. "What is it?" she said. "What's the matter?" She reached to touch my forehead.

It was as if she were my mother. I angled away from her hands and her face. The sadness was gone, and now all I could feel was the tickling of violence. The ailment was in me. I wanted it, the screaming and the smashing, the broken plates and picture frames.

I had to leave before it happened. There were errands, I said, some shopping I promised to do with my mother. "Now?" she said. "But you've come all this way."

It took her a few minutes to recover, to understand. Then she figured it out. Her voice assumed its flippant office pitch. "Oh, well," she said in English. "Thanks for coming."

In December, our company had layoffs, and Nadya was among the first ones to go, due to her lack of seniority. Our coworkers said it was a shame. They took her to a downtown restaurant with opera-singing waiters. The waiters entertained them with Russian "Kalinka" (at Nadya's request) and with something from Pavarotti. That's what our coworkers had told me. I myself hadn't gone.

We rarely spoke anymore, and when we did, it was about work. I thought she took our separation lightly. She'd cobbled up some last-minute office alliances. She went out to lunches a lot. I tried not to think of that day at her house.

On her last day, she stopped at my cubicle. She wore a dress made of clingy material, and her belly was starting to show now, a gentle swelling, so natural and strange on her otherwise spindly body. She brought me Russian candy, a gluey caramel, Moo-Moo. I thanked her and put the candy in my mouth. She smiled. There was a speck of caramel stuck to her tooth.

I wanted to tell her I loved her.

Instead, I told her I'd applied to business schools. "I know you'll get in," said Nadya. She seemed sincere, as if she understood how crooked I felt. "You need to get out of here," she said. And for a moment I could see it, too, the liberated version of myself, somewhere in a college town, in a wintry Midwestern state.

I wrote to Polina that day. I'd never replied to her letter, but now, months later, I had to. I told her I'd made a mistake, and though it was too late to mend it, I wanted her to understand. I wrote to her about my fears and my parents, the years in America, my grad school plans. I even wrote about Nadya.

At night I dreamed about them. Two girls, all stalky lines and flowing hair. We were in my old Moscow apartment, and I was begging them to stay. They couldn't. Their shapes were getting paler, their laughter faint. *The past is behind us,* they said. Snowflakes spiraled down.

Snake Oil

Mandy stood in front of the open garage and asked her husband why anybody would ask her over for lunch on a Sunday. Dan was already moving the bicycles, hanging the rakes on a hook, stacking things she didn't recognize. Maybe this woman wanted to get to know her, be her friend, he said, rolling up the garden hoses.

"Don't be so suspicious of people," he said. He pulled up his socks and straightened his back, rolling his broad shoulders. His hair was graying, and when she saw his crooked teeth, she couldn't tell if he was smiling or wincing with pain. He had set out to clean up.

Mandy first met the woman's husband at the hospital where she worked. He was a heart surgeon, a gentle Indian man with chocolate eyes who sympathized with Mandy being the only woman in her orthopedic practice. His wife was also from India, and she was new in town.

Maybe Dan was right. Maybe the heart doctor's wife did just want to get to know her. Then maybe Mandy was right from the start. Here was someone new in town who needed a friend. But Mandy could be mistaken, too. She was making mistakes lately, not in surgery, but at home. Small mistakes, like putting the peanut butter in the freezer and the fudgecicles in the pantry. And when her decorator asked her over the phone, *What kind of furniture is in your bedroom?* Mandy thought she said, *What kind of failure is in your bedroom?*

Mandy hated going out on a Sunday, her only day off that week, but she told Dan, *Okay, maybe you are right, think positive, right?* She couldn't help herself liking the idea that this woman had singled her out as a potential woman friend.

She wore a dress and boots. She never wore dresses. She wore pants to work, running shoes for surgery. The dress was the same light brown color as her hair, and when she saw that she looked tall and fit, her neck long and white, she told herself she should wear this dress more often. It made her pretty and feminine. It was very much a lady's luncheon dress. She thought of the luncheons her grandmother used to give, Southern luncheons with linens and china and silver dishes filled with butter mints. Back then, when she saw the dishes and the ladies all dressed up, Mandy felt different about her sixteen-year-old life. She had left her mother and her bad stepfather behind, and with these good grandparents she saw how she could change, how she could make herself different. Better.

She thought of cutting flowers from the garden to bring to the woman from India. But the roses in the garden were spent, and all the flowering perennials her sister, Clara, and the children planted were long gone. Already there had been three hard frosts. Every morning in the early purple hours of dawn there was frost on the ground when she left for work. Soon it would snow. But today, today the sun was out, and she only needed a light jacket.

She stopped off at the grocery store and bought a pot of mums—the orange and yellow ones that looked like daisies and cost $10.99, not the simple yellow ones on sale for $5.99.

The woman's house was huge, gaudy, very brick, and masculine, and the inside smelled of curry and chickpeas. At the doorway, Mandy embraced the hostess, who was just as pretty as Mandy remembered her to be. She had light brown skin and beautifully shaped eyebrows. Mandy felt as awkward as a prom date when she gave her hostess the mums. She said the hostess's name, which came out sounding like Sangria.

"It's Sanjana," she said, laughing. "It means soft and meek. My husband's name means Chief Veda god. Ridiculous, yes?" They stood back and smiled at one another until at last, seeing Sanjana's jeans and flip-flops, Mandy knew.

"You look so beautiful," Sanjana said. "We've set up downstairs. We'll eat and talk about health. You know."

Mandy tried hard not to feel too tall in her high boots and overdressed in her dressy dress as Sanjana led the way downstairs, where the cooking smells grew stronger and more curried. Mandy saw oil paintings on every wall along the way, the kind of oil paintings you see in good foreign-hotel waiting areas near a front desk. Brass glinted from the staircase and from behind glass cabinets.

There was a kitchen downstairs and upstairs, Sanjana explained. It was that kind of house. Mandy kept smiling, careful to say the right things at the right times about the good smells, the countertops, the ping-pong table, and the view of the lake.

The basement looked out onto the woods with all the leaves now red and gold. It was a beautiful view. Sanjana had set up almost thirty green and white plastic chairs. In the middle of the room, near the brown leather sofas, two women fiddled with a laptop and a projector for what looked to be a PowerPoint presentation. They looked up as they introduced themselves, checking out Mandy's dress. They were both named Nancy, and they were both wearing tight jeans.

More than anything, Mandy wished she had not worn the dress, not because she didn't like it, but because she stood out so.

She introduced herself, sticking out her hand. "I'm going to the philharmonic later," she lied, already wishing she hadn't said anything. The Nancys nodded and went back to their laptop.

Sanjana was setting up a card table covered with a green polyester cloth, and Mandy offered to help. They each held one end, and the cloth ballooned its way down on the tabletop, reminding Mandy of a scene from an old movie she saw a long time ago. In it, a maid and an older woman with a mustache—a woman who later in the movie becomes a man—were making up a bed. It was a silly thing to think of just then, and Mandy thought better than to mention it to Sanjana.

Sanjana asked Mandy to open some of the lotions, oils, and cosmetics and put them all on the table.

Mandy thought of what a friend had said when dealing with a difficult vegan who would not eat what she served because of the kind of oil she cooked with. Her friend said, "So we're down to the oils, are we?" She was glad she had this thought because it made her smile. We're down to the oils. It was important to keep smiling here. The card table full of lotions and oils, all opened and desperate to be sampled, made her want to weep. She hated to think of Sanjana peddling this stuff.

"How did you get into this?" Mandy finally asked.

"This?" Sanjana said. "I really believe in these products. They're really amazing."

Mandy searched Sanjana's pretty face to see if she was earnest. How could she "believe" in lotions?

"I also wanted to make some money of my own. You know, to have. So that I am not constantly calling the Chief to see if I can buy a scarf or a skirt." She laughed, but Mandy noticed now her laugh was a nervous laugh.

More women came. Mandy recognized them as doctors' wives and one an administrator from one of the private elementary schools. There were about ten of them in all. Mandy felt sorry for Sanjana, who obviously had expected more people. She wondered if Sanjana had had a difficult time rounding up this group of women to come to her basement on a Sunday, but these women did not seem to mind. They seemed so much better prepared for the event. They were all wearing jeans, and they came in laughing and talking about what their children said. They laughed as if they were always on vacation. In high voices, they talked about their wardrobes, what they would feed their families that night, their living-room window treatments, and what was and what was not expected to bloom in their perennial beds. Mandy could smell them waiting for her to say something.

She smiled, trying to think of something, but she had nothing to say. She sat on a slippery leather sofa and pretended to read a pamphlet about vitamins.

Mandy wished she had worn her beeper. She would have made it go off right then. Then she could have excused herself in a brisk, efficient way. The women would not like her for it, but they would have to force themselves to understand. They would think and say that she was *that* kind of woman, the kind who always left early. She was nothing like them, more like their husbands.

At least they ate first. Sanjana served everything from the bar. It was a strange, wonderful combination of food on a Sunday afternoon: chopped vegetable soup, which was delicious, oily and spicy; buttery yellowed potatoes; black chick peas and basmati rice; a salad with bottled dressing; water. The food was served on Styrofoam plates with dividers. Eating the food made Mandy even hungrier, and she marveled at Sanjana's ease. She had cooked everything.

One of the Nancys started talking as they ate. She wore a feathery boa, and she told them about how the lotion company sent her to California and Hawaii and how soon she would get a Mercedes. She spoke of all the estrogen they ingested unknowingly from cows, chickens, and eggs injected with hormones. She talked of poisons, pesticides, and plastics. They continued to eat and listen, their Styrofoam plates squeaking with every bite. The other Nancy began to speak as the first, boaed Nancy stood up and tiptoed away, upstairs and out the door.

Mandy heard a car door open and shut. She wondered what the boaed Nancy drove as she awaited her Mercedes and how much lotion she would have to sell to get the car of her dreams. She wondered if this Nancy was also married to a "chief."

Downstairs in the basement, as they finished eating what they could of Sanjana's good food, the other Nancy closed the curtains and dimmed the lights as she told them what the extra estrogen was doing to them—making them fat and irritable, giving them tender breasts, fibroid tumors, uterine cancer, painful periods, terrible cramping, and night sweats. She started the PowerPoint presentation, showing pictures of overweight, irritable-looking women.

Hadn't they noticed the older they got, the thicker their middles were getting? Hesitantly, a few of the women nodded, putting their plastic forks down. That was the estrogen, Nancy said. The women swallowed their food. All of them stopped eating.

"And I just thought that was because I ate half my son's Halloween candy," Mandy said.

The other women turned and laughed. Finally she had said something, and it was even funny. A two-fer, as her husband would say. She felt the women let out their breaths as they smiled at her. She was known for this sort of thing in and out of surgical rooms. It made her one of the guys in her practice, and now here, she was one of the gals. And Mandy felt more than ever that these women needed someone like her to say something like that. They needed protection from this Nancy, who was obviously building up some kind of argument that had everything to do with making them feel bad about their bodies.

The other Nancy smiled, flashed a close-up picture of some woman struggling with sit-ups, then went on with her estrogen stories. She told them about her daughter's early periods and struggle with weight gain. When she told them about her mother-in-law's dry vagina, Mandy vowed not to say anything more. This

Nancy had topped her and won with her mother-in-law's dry vagina, which hushed them all. Sanjana got up to clear the plates, and the situation grew hopeless. Nancy went on to tell them about her husband's fear of prostate cancer. She told them that the solution to all these problems was the lotion in the blue bottle. She held up the lotion in the blue bottle for them all to see.

The lotion in the blue bottle balanced out your hormones. The lotion in the blue bottle was the antidote to all the estrogen.

Nancy said one pump was pre-measured and it was all you needed, once a night on the twelfth day of your cycle. She showed them how to count from the first day of their last period, as if they didn't already know of such things. She said that some women use the lotion and feel its effects right away. She said it was best to use at night, because it could make you drowsy, but it wasn't dangerous.

"You could bathe in this stuff, and the worst thing that could happen is that you would be very relaxed, happy, and sleepy."

She went on to show how you spread the lotion on the parts of your body with the thinnest skin—your face, wrists, inner arms and thighs. Mandy grew more and more impatient, but when Nancy explained where to spread the lotion, Mandy immediately thought how lovely it would feel now to spread lotion on her inner thigh.

The lotion in the blue bottle was made of wild yams. Mandy thought Nancy said something also about ginger, soy beans, and lemongrass, but she lost track. She was thinking about the lotion on her inner thighs and what that might cure.

Mandy recalled a healer who had come to town two or three years back. He was a well-known priest from Ireland, and a Catholic friend of Dan's called to say this priest would be at a nearby church, healing. He thought they might be interested. She had wondered why the Catholic friend thought they might be interested. But they were interested, and while her sister, Clara, stayed with the children, Mandy and Dan went to the healing at the church.

She had not been to Mass for years, and she was glad that there was no communion because she didn't have to debate whether or not to receive the host, even though she would have just in case it mattered.

It had been on a weeknight. She listened hard to words she never heard around the operating table: *grace, transfigure, abounding, mercy*. There were catchers—volunteer men who stood behind each person as they stood in line and stepped up to the priest. Mandy thought that was a nice touch, to have the catchers. The priest said something in Latin, then touched each person on the forehead.

Mandy and her husband stood in the line with all the others.

"Just to see," she said to Dan.

"It can't hurt," Dan said.

There were hundreds there. People she had never seen before. Soon though, she began to recognize some of her patients.

Edna Berridge stood patiently leaning on her cane. Her broken foot had not healed, and at sixty-three, she was miserable knowing that perhaps she would never be right again. Gary Howlit shuffled up with his walker. He refused physical therapy, and Mandy had given up nagging him about it.

The priest touched Dan's forehead first, and it looked as though the priest was trying to push him with his thumb. Nothing happened, Dan just stared at the priest, then stepped back to wait for Mandy.

The priest said something Mandy could no longer remember, and he looked her in the eye. He looked kind with all the lines around his mouth and blue eyes. He looked fun and kind and as though he laughed and drank beer a great deal. Mandy had wanted to start up a conversation then, ask if he liked Joyce. He touched her forehead with his thumb. She closed her eyes. She felt something, though she did not know what. She thought the priest looked disappointed that she did not fall back. She thought perhaps the catcher behind her might be disappointed, too, so she leaned back a little as if to fall, only in order to please them both. The catcher put a hand to her back as though to prop her up.

All around the altar in front of them, people, mostly women, were lying down on the floor, where their catchers had laid them, their eyes closed, their arms spread out like wings. Were they sleeping? Dreaming? Swooning? Faking it? Their faces looked so relaxed and calm. She felt terrible, but she couldn't help but think they looked as though they had just had wonderful sex. And she recalled some class she took in college. Some student had insisted that there was a period of time when good sex led you to some sort of spiritual awakening. Discussion had ensued on exactly when that period of time was.

Mandy recognized one of the women on the floor at the foot of the altar. This woman had sold them their house. Mandy heard she had been diagnosed with pancreatic cancer, and that the woman even joked to clients that at long last she would lose some weight. Seeing her lying there, Mandy hoped that maybe, just maybe, the healer would heal this woman and she could go back to selling houses and saying all those funny, irreverent things she was fond of saying.

Later, in the car on the way home, full of energy, Mandy asked Dan if he had felt anything.

"*Nada*," he said, pulling into their driveway, pressing the button on the visor that opened the garage door. "You?"

"Something. There was something. I'm almost positive."

"Yeah?" Dan said, getting out of the car, bumping his knee on a child's bike.

"Yeah. It was like I went away for a nano-second, you know? Like I went up to the ceiling. But I don't know if that's because I *wanted* something to happen."

He looked at her and nodded. "Huh. Maybe wanting something to happen combines with what happens to make something happen."

She laughed and said, "Maybe."

They looked around the lit-up garage. "We've got to clean out this place," he said.

One month later, Mandy read the real estate agent's obituary in the morning paper. The woman had sold houses for twenty years and had been in a book group for as many years. Mandy had liked this woman, had meant to get together with her after they bought the house. She had wanted to be this woman's friend. She could have been in the woman's book group. Mandy missed reading, and she had so few women friends.

Nancy was showing them a green bottle of lotion now. She said to use this lotion if you had had a hysterectomy. She used words like *detox, balance, sensitivity, redefine,* and *self-adjust.* Her words were like keys that unlocked stories and ailments from the women sitting in the room. All at once, they spoke of their aches and pains in a now-that-you-mention-it-I-have-a-secret-too kind of way.

Mandy thought of the construction worker who came into her office that week with an ache he couldn't explain. He sat on Mandy's new examination table sturdy enough for her obese patients, and he held up his scarred wrist. "I had a stick that went in here and came out here," he said. "Sometimes it pains me."

"Yes," she said, gently turning his arm. "I imagine it would."

Once upon a time, maybe Mandy and these women-wives would have been sitting around exchanging recipes, Tupperware, playing bridge, or discussing books. Now here she was in this basement, sitting with pretty ladies complaining and worrying about growing old, wrinkled, and finding aches and deteriorations that were possibly yet to be found or felt.

When Nancy had finished talking, Mandy looked at her watch and hoisted herself up from the leather sofa. Her back hurt. She wished she hadn't worn the high-heeled boots. Sanjana stood up, too, from her green plastic chair. "I hope you weren't too bored?"

Mandy wanted to tell her, well, no, she was more angry than bored. In her mind, she had the speech prepared: She had not wanted to hear about Nancy's family's medical traumas. She thought the whole talk was disgusting—did men do this? No, they most certainly did not. She wanted to say, Bored? No. Disappointed, perhaps.

She got out her wallet instead. "How much is the blue lotion?"

The sky turned on the drive home, with bone-colored clouds threatening rain or snow, she knew not which. She had done her residency near Austin, Texas, and had learned there to hate the cold.

When she got home, Dan stood at the kitchen counter tucking garlic and fresh rosemary under the skins of two chickens. Mandy didn't say a word about estrogen. She gave Clara a gift bag containing the lotion in the blue bottle. She had bought two bottles, and Sanjana had hugged her, looking heartbreakingly grateful. Mandy had almost wisecracked then, "Look, I just bought some lotion. I'm not joining your cult or anything." But she held back, and she thanked Sanjana for the lovely afternoon instead.

"Oh my God, people swear by this stuff," her sister said, thanking Mandy, hugging the bottle to her. "I've heard all about this. Very California, very in." Clara went on about all that she had heard from infomercials and such about the special natural lipsticks and herbal bath soaps the company made. Mandy thought then that she probably had not done enough for Clara. Clara had, after all, given up the apartment downtown to come live with them and take care of their children, Allegra and Zach, while she and Dan worked. She should have taken Clara to the luncheon with her, in fact. Clara would have gotten up and left when she saw the laptop and the green chairs all in a row, then they could have gone to the cheap Mexican place down the street to drink margaritas.

While the chickens baked, Clara opened a bottle of good wine and poured it out into the good crystal glasses. Mandy could joke now about her afternoon, and she made Dan and Clara both laugh, imitating the women. The whole house smelled of cooking. She tossed a salad in a glass bowl with vinaigrette Clara made.

When the chickens had cooled and Dan carved them, he did not once say anything about her being the surgeon and when was she going to learn to carve. Mandy even kissed the back of his neck. His sweat tasted as salty as smoked salmon.

He had been her teacher at one point. In medical school, he taught Gross Anatomy, and when she had landed the job with a private practice, he willingly moved and taught classes at the local university, pleased to have more time for research, cooking, and gardening. When they moved to Chicago, they were giddy with excitement over their new lives. They often drove downtown without the children, walked to the Oak Street Beach, and spent whole evenings kissing and climbing on each other in the sand.

Neither Allegra nor Zach were watching TV or playing video games. Clara had given them baths and combed their hair, and she now had Allegra setting the table in the dining room for a change. When they all sat down, Zach got to light the candles, and they said ahh. It was a Sunday night, and they were having a Sunday dinner. They could hear the wind blowing the dried leaves outside, and something wailed in the chimney, making the children draw closer.

The chicken was perfect, and Zach showed them how to act like a man by slamming his hand on the table and saying, "Oh man." On any other night, the slamming, the shaking water glasses, the stereotyping, would have annoyed Mandy, but she laughed with the others and wondered out loud if he could imitate women as well.

After two glasses of wine, Mandy thought of her Monday schedule, and her teeth ached to think of all the surgeries. Two hip replacements in the morning, and another in the afternoon. Then there would be all the surprise visits, the motorcycle accidents, and always the plant managers bringing in workers from the factories. Her week was booked solid with patients, people she barely even recognized as people anymore. She used to love her work fixing people, piecing them back together. But she couldn't take pleasure in how she changed them anymore. Now she could only think of the years of work ahead of her and how it—how the work—would change her and wear her down.

Mandy covered the top of her glass with her hand when Dan offered her more wine.

While Clara put the children to bed, Mandy helped Dan with the dishes, then took a long, steamy shower. When she got out, she looked in the mirror at her cloudy reflection, glad not to see herself clearly, just her hair pulled back, wet and black, the loose, pinkened skin, and of course, the thickening middle. She hadn't gone to the health club in weeks.

How to use this body. She made a mental list: strengthen in order to power saw through skin and bone in order to insert, fit, and snap in new hips, knees, and joints. When necessary, keep clothed expensively to fit in and feel superior. Otherwise, cover at all times with lab coat and stethoscope to blend in with boy doctors.

She dried herself, going on with the list. Clean and dry gently, then polish smooth for desired effect. She took the plastic cap off the lotion in the blue bottle. She pressed the top down one, two, then three times, until at last she saw the white lotion coming out into one carefully measured dollop in her left hand.

She first dabbed then rubbed some of the lotion on her breasts. She put some on her inner arms and finally on her inner thighs. For balance, the instructions said.

She thought of Sanjana's face and that line from that Ezra Pound haiku: *Petals on a wet, black bough.* She thought of her children on their bicycles with Clara, and she thought of Dan leaning back in the sand, his hands on her hips. She said his name and felt yellow moonlight melting all around.

She could barely breathe with all the feeling she had. She put both hands on the counter, and then closed her eyes. She was dizzy with something, and she thought she heard a steady hum in her ears, or was that the chimney again? When she caught her breath, she opened her eyes, recognizing the sound, the place. Winter was coming, and it was getting cold.

ALIX OHLIN

The Only Child

It all started when Sophie came home from college, between her sophomore and junior years. She wasn't happy to be back. She'd grown to love Boston, the sad blustery winters, the confusing one-ways and roundabouts, and she felt like she'd outgrown California—its sunny, childlike happiness. Worst of all was her mother. Sophie was an only child, and her mother had always clung to her. She tiptoed into her room at night to watch her sleep. As a child Sophie hadn't noticed, but now that she was older she usually wasn't asleep yet when her mother came into the room, and she'd look up from her book and say, "*What* are you looking at?"

Which only made her mother smile affectionately and back out of the room. By late June Sophie couldn't take it anymore; she went over to her friend Beena's house, and they called up Trevor, the drug connection from high school, and got a dime bag and some ecstasy, and suddenly it was four o'clock in the morning, and Sophie drove home at breakneck speed only to find her parents still up, waiting.

"You guys," she said, "you're driving me crazy."

Her mother was crying.

"It's not that bad," Sophie said. "I was just out late. At school I do this all the time. I mean, not all the time. But, you know what I mean."

"We have to tell you something," her father said. "We should have told you a long time ago." He was a serious man, her father, prone to ominous pronouncements regarding issues he had no ability to affect. "This real estate bubble will burst very soon," he'd say while barbecuing chicken. Or: "The tax code has become so complex that the ordinary person cannot hope to figure it out."

So Sophie wasn't all that concerned when she sat down to hear what they had to say. She hadn't steeled herself for any news in particular, and this (in addition to the drugs) was probably why, in the future, she could never remember the exact words in which her parents told her that she was not, after all, an only child.

She had an older brother, and he'd been given up for adoption, and they'd never known where he was all these years.

"We were very young," her mother said. "We weren't married. You didn't know my parents, Sophie, but they were very strict. We had the baby, then gave him up. Eventually we got married and had you, and that was wonderful. But I've thought about him every day since he was born. I was so happy when we got the letter today, saying he wanted to meet us."

At this point she had to stop talking, because she was crying so hard. She could barely breathe. Sophie crossed the room and sat down next to her mother, who melted against her shoulder. On the other side of her, Sophie's father held her hand.

The brother she'd never known existed was named Philip. He lived in New York City and was an investment banker. His adoptive parents had given him a good life, with good schools, with love. He didn't want anything from Sophie and her family, just to meet them. Her mother wrote back, saying they would love to meet, telling him about Sophie. Two weeks later the phone rang. Philip was going to be in L.A. on business the following week. He wanted to meet, but not at the house. Her mother said they'd all be there.

The day of the meeting Sophie's mother put on and discarded every item of clothing in her closet. Sophie was wearing a T-shirt and jeans, and it was her father, who ordinarily never noticed her appearance, who asked her to change into something a little nicer. "This occasion," he said, "will be something we remember forever. Not many days are like that, pumpkin."

So she wore a dress. She still hadn't decided how she felt about anything. She'd never thought about having a brother. She'd always wanted a sister, someone to confide in, to whisper with at night after the lights were out. Someone mischievous and fun, down to earth, not dreamy like her mother—though now she understood what her mother had been dreaming about, all this time.

They waited at a Taco Bell on the freeway, holding medium-sized Pepsis. All three of them always ordered mediums, never smalls or larges. They were a family that took the middle road.

The door opened, and a man in a suit came in and stood looking around. Her mother gasped. Sophie felt a strong wind shake her arms and spine, a buffeting force. Red hair, green eyes, freckles, a square face, a round nose, a flush on the cheeks, one line that cut straight across the forehead. All this time there had been someone in the world who looked exactly like her.

Philip came towards them, unsmiling, and sat down. "This is awkward," he said. "Hello."

"I know," Sophie's mother said, then bit her lower lip.

Sophie leaned forward. "Would you like something? We have drinks, I could get you something."

He looked at her—she saw it register on his face, how exactly alike they looked—and smiled stiffly. "Sure," he said. "Root beer, a large? Thanks."

Sophie felt stung. She hated root beer. Of course she understood this meant nothing, but another part of her thought it meant everything. The situation made everything symbolic, made everything, even root beer, carry too much weight.

When she got back to the table her parents and Philip were talking about the weather. They didn't seem able to move any deeper into the conversation, to say the things they wanted to say. She sat there feeling annoyed with all of them, with the spindly artifice of small talk. She didn't realize that there were some things that couldn't be said and that these were the most important things, and that everyone except her knew it. When she married her first husband, Lars, ten years later, she would tell him constantly, effusively, how much she loved him and how much he meant to her. And Lars would hold her hand and nod, and his silence would drive her crazy, so crazy after a while that she went off and slept with his best friend and business partner, Joe, who was short and squat and called her "Cookie" in bed, and the act wasn't even finished before she started hating herself and him. Afterwards she came home and found Lars sitting in the living room with a drink. She could either tell him or not tell him. She still loved him. Instead of telling him she stopped taking her birth control pills and got pregnant, and that's how they had Sara. During her pregnancy Lars broke off his business partnership with Joe, even though it left them at a terrible financial disadvantage, and Sophie was so angry at this—they were going to have a child, they needed to be stable, there were house and car payments to think about—and also hormonal, that she cried and raged and threatened to leave him. And Lars said, in his muted way, "But I have to. Don't you see?"

She understood then that he had known about her and Joe all along, and that breaking off the partnership was his way of trying for a fresh start. And she was so grateful, and she wanted it to work so badly; but it didn't.

This was later. At the time, at Taco Bell, she had no idea how the small talk was protecting them from all the scabrous weight of the past. All she knew was that her mother asked Philip the story of his life, and he told it, and then her parents talked about their business, Sophie's college in Boston, their house, even the perennials they were trying to grow in the garden. It was a conversation people might have on an airplane.

As they were leaving, Philip turned to her. "You and I live so close to each other," he said. "You should come visit me, in the fall, when you go back to school."

"I don't know," Sophie said. Her mother, who hadn't wanted her to live in a coed dorm, who worried when Sophie took a cab from her dorm room to the airport on her way home, was nodding vehemently.

"You can stay with me and my girlfriend. I'll tease you and pull your hair, or whatever a big brother is supposed to do. We'll figure it out. You'll like Fiona, she's nice. All this was actually her idea, me getting in touch with you guys."

"Oh," Sophie's mother said softly, as if punched.

"Not that I hadn't thought about it myself," he said.

Sophie went back to school, and in October, for Columbus Day weekend, she went to New York. She'd been there once before, with her roommate, who was from Long Island. They stayed in the suburbs, and during their one day in Manhattan they went to FAO Schwartz. This time she took a taxi from the train station to the Upper West Side, where her brother—saying it, inside her mind, still gave her an intense, but not entirely unpleasant, horror-movie shiver—lived. They'd arranged this on the phone.

"I'll still be at work when you get here," Philip had said. "But Fiona will let you in and entertain you until dinner."

"Okay," Sophie said.

"We'll show you a good time, don't worry," he said. "And we can call your mom on the phone while you're here, so she knows you're all right."

Sophie wondered why he said *your* mom. But of course he had his own mom, who lived in Philadelphia and was a banker like him. His dad was an orthodontist.

The building's doorman asked Sophie's name, made a call, then carried her backpack to the elevator and pressed the button, as if the exertion would be too much for her fingers. Upstairs, Fiona waited with the door open, smiling. She looked like a movie star, with straight, glossy brown hair and manicured fingernails. Grabbing Sophie's backpack, she threw her arm around Sophie's shoulder and gently pushed her into the apartment, all the while offering drinks, food, a shower.

"We'll make up the couch for you later," she said. "I'm sorry there isn't a spare room, but this is New York. We all live like sardines. We're going to move soon, I swear, it's just such a nightmare looking for a place. Have a seat. It's so great to meet you. God, you look just like him, don't you? Didn't that freak you out?"

It was the first time anyone had mentioned the weirdness of the situation to her. Everyone else, her parents, her new brother, seemed intent on making the situation ordinary, which it manifestly wasn't. At this onslaught of honesty Sophie felt grateful, and close to tears.

"It's incredibly weird," she said.

"Must be," Fiona said. "But also good, right? I mean, here you have somebody else in the world who's part of your family. Somebody else to care for you."

Sophie honestly hadn't thought about it that way at all. "I guess I'm still getting used to it," she said.

At eight, she and Fiona went out to a French restaurant. Her brother arrived twenty minutes late, trailing a briefcase and apologies. Then he insisted on ordering for her.

"Have you had oysters?" he asked. "What about snails? Have you had steak tartar, ever, in your life? I bet you didn't have snails growing up in California."

She hadn't, and she didn't want them now, but thought it would be rude to refuse. She thought he was testing her. She didn't realize that he felt he had something to prove, that he thought his entire life—what he'd been given, what he'd become—was under scrutiny. Fiona sat back and didn't talk much, just smiled at both of them. Philip ordered the snails and a bottle of Bordeaux, and Fiona pushed her glass over to Sophie, letting her drink most of it. Philip kept asking her questions. What was the house like where she grew up, what kind of after-school activities did she do, what kind of high school did she attend, what did she get on her SATs. It felt like a job interview.

"You must be smart, you go to a good college," he said. "What are you going to do after you graduate? You could move to New York. I could help you. I have some connections. The world is about connections, you know. It's something I didn't realize when I was in college, but it's totally true."

"I was thinking maybe grad school?" Sophie said. She didn't want to let go of the world she'd only just discovered. It was the first place she'd felt like an adult, and she couldn't imagine that there would be other places she might feel that way, other ways she could grow up.

Philip laughed. "Everybody here is either just dropping out of grad school or just about to go back. You'll fit in perfectly."

He ordered dessert for the table but didn't eat any himself. Sophie and Fiona shared it, their two spoons digging into the meringue. She was close enough to smell Fiona's perfume, noticed a diamond engagement ring on her left hand.

The next day, Fiona offered Sophie a menu of activities: the Guggenheim, MoMA, the Met. Sophie said, "We don't have to do anything big and touristy. Just walking around is good."

Fiona smiled. "That's such a mature thing to say. It's so true that you see more of a city that way." Sophie felt that she'd done well. "Let's go to Chinatown, and then we can have coffee and dessert in Little Italy, maybe walk around SoHo. How does that sound?"

"Perfect," Sophie said.

They took a cab downtown. The streets in Chinatown were mobbed. While holding hands with Philip, Fiona pointed things out to Sophie: Chanel knock-off purses, an art supply store, ducks hanging in windows. Next they moved over to Little Italy, where they had lunch. All the talk was about New York, what it was like to live there, the difficulties and advantages of it, the rents, the stresses. It was like some urban version of her parents' friends sitting around talking about their houses. Sophie felt wise, having this revelation. She thought that this was maturity, the ability to see through people. It was only later she found out that anyone could see through people, and the hard thing was not to try.

After lunch Fiona said she was tired, and they went back to the apartment. She told Sophie that she was going to take a nap, and suggested that Sophie and Philip call California.

It was one in the afternoon there, and Sophie's mother was outside gardening. "Are you having a good time?" she asked, her voice a little breathless.

"Of course," Sophie said, knowing that this was what she wanted to hear, yet unable to bring herself to rave, to brim over with stories.

"Put him on?" her mother said.

Sophie motioned to her brother. He stood with the receiver pressed to his ear, smiling a polite smile. Was he good-looking? Sophie couldn't say. His face was long, like hers; his nose had a bump in it. If she'd passed him on the street, without knowing, would she have noticed him, would she have felt him somehow?

"Soph," her brother said. He was still smiling, but now he held out the phone.

When she picked it up she could hear her mother crying. "Are you okay?"

"I'm great," said her mother, the worst liar ever. "I'm just so happy."

In the background she could hear her father speaking but not the specific words. Whatever they were, he was trying to comfort her, she knew. In the future, after he retired, this comforting tendency of her father's would grow even stronger. He'd start cooking for her mother, even breakfast, even when she got sick. He'd shadow her from room to room, just as Sophie's mother had once done to her. Her mother, irritable from pain, would complain about this to Sophie while her father was in the kitchen straining broth into homemade soup. After her death, of liver cancer, Sophie would expect him to fade into shadow himself, to lose his purpose, or to move into her own home—she would be living with her second husband at the time, and sharing custody of Sara with Lars and custody of Mark's son, Henry, with his ex-wife, a rotating parade of schedules and children that had to be carefully marked and updated on wall calendars lest total chaos ensue—but he seemed happy in his own routine, walking two miles each day, following the news. It was not until this time that she understood her father was the most self-sufficient person she had ever known, and that her mother, the doter, the worrier, the maker of phone calls, had been the most in need of care.

"It's okay, Mom," Sophie said now. "We're having a nice time."

"Please remember everything," her mother said, "and tell me later?"

"I'll try," Sophie said. She hung up the phone and looked for Philip—she wanted to commiserate, a glance to pass between them—but he was in the kitchen already, talking to Fiona, pouring himself a glass of wine.

They were supposed to go out to dinner again, but Philip had drunk two glasses of wine and said he was tired. He wanted to order Chinese instead and stay home. It sounded fine to Sophie, but Fiona didn't like the idea. "Sophie's only in town for one weekend," she said. "We should be taking her to the Russian Tea Room or something."

"The Russian Tea Room's closed down, babe," Philip said, a touch of irritation in his voice.

"I said or something."

"And anyway, she's cool with it. Right?"

Sophie nodded slightly, afraid of committing too much to his side of the disagreement. When her parents fought, they did so in their bedroom, at night, keeping their voices down and the door closed. She was thirteen before she figured out that they ever disagreed on anything, although this, she now knew, was the least of their secrets.

"Of course she's *cool with it,*" Fiona said. She was standing with her arms folded in front of her, and Sophie couldn't be sure but it seemed like tears were glimmering in her eyes. "She doesn't know what the other options are. That's why we should come up with something. You always want to do the *least difficult* thing."

"And that's wrong?" Philip said. He poured himself another glass of wine, clearly an act of defiance. There was a kind of electrical current in the room, like just before a thunderstorm, a too-hot wind.

Fiona started to cry. Sophie wished for somewhere else to go, but there was no other room. Just their bedroom, and she couldn't very well go in there. "We can do whatever," she said. "I'm easy."

The other woman looked at her, and tried to smile. "You're such a sweetheart," she said bitterly. "It's hard to believe you're related."

"Hey," Philip said.

Sophie tried again. "Maybe we could have dinner here, and then you and I could do something," she told Fiona. "A movie or something, there must be tons of stuff I couldn't see anywhere else."

"This isn't about you and me spending time together," Fiona said.

Sophie stepped back. And then stepped back again, to sit down.

"You get these ideas, and you can't handle any deviation," her brother said. "Everything has to go according to your plan."

"There's nothing wrong with having a plan. If you don't have a plan you don't get anywhere," Fiona said.

"Maybe I like where I am," her brother said.

"I have to push you to do everything. If it weren't for me you'd never do anything. You'd just live here alone for the rest of your life," Fiona said. "That's what you want, isn't?"

"It's looking pretty good right about now," Philip said.

Fiona went into the bedroom, leaving Sophie and her brother alone.

Philip ordered Chinese without asking her what she wanted, and the two of them watched basketball. He switched to beer and gave her one, which she drank quickly. The second she pulled out of the fridge herself without asking. An hour later Fiona came out of the bedroom carrying her jacket and walked straight out the door without saying anything.

"Are you going after her?" Sophie said. Her brother shrugged.

"She can take care of herself," he said.

Sophie thought of her parents worrying every time she left the house, how her mother sometimes called her first thing in the morning at school, as if she might not have survived the night; she thought about how they both cried when they left her in Boston at the beginning of college, Sophie herself dry-eyed, itching to be alone. She walked out of the apartment—"Hey," Philip said, but that was the extent of his interference—rode the elevator down, and stood in the street wondering where Fiona had gone. Though it was late there were still tons of people out, walking around, there were cabs and cars. A person could go anywhere and do anything. It was cold. Nobody looked at her; nobody asked what she was doing. Helpless, wordless, she went back inside. By the time she went to sleep on the couch, Fiona still hadn't come home.

Her train wasn't until noon, and Sophie woke up wondering how she was going to get through the last few hours of the visit. But Fiona and Philip were in the kitchen making French toast. Sitting up, she saw that Philip had his arms around Fiona's waist, and Fiona was laughing, a low, sweet murmur of a laugh. Then they started kissing. Sophie's parents had never fought in front of her, and they'd never kissed in front of her, either, and she approved of this discretion, completely. As she watched, Fiona took one of Philip's hands and moved it so that his palm lay flat on her stomach. Holding it, she rubbed it against herself, as if she were a magic lamp or a special prize.

She faked sleep until Fiona shook her shoulder gently. Together they stripped the couch, folding the blanket the way Sophie had learned in Girl Scouts, where Fiona held one end and Sophie walked the other end up to her and pressed it to her chest. Fiona's eyes sparkled at Sophie when the two of them stood close, face to face.

"Thanks for coming to look for me last night," she said.

"Oh, it was nothing."

"It's not nothing. He learned something from you. He doesn't understand things sometimes, because of how he grew up. He thinks everybody chooses who they love."

Sophie didn't know what this meant, but nodded as if she did.

Then Philip served the French toast. He was in a great mood and kept telling Sophie that she should come back, that the couch would be reserved for her.

"Consider it your pied-à-terre," he told her. Once again she didn't know what this was, but she knew that knowing it was a source of pride to him. In the three days they'd spent together she'd only gotten to know this much about him.

The three of them ate breakfast while reading the newspaper. After a while Sophie took a shower and packed her bag. She was already thinking about school, the party she'd missed by being here, what she would say to her mother when she called that night.

"Hey, what are you doing for Thanksgiving?" Philip said. "You could come back here, with us."

"I'm supposed to go home," Sophie said. "Why don't you guys come out there? Mom and Dad would love it."

"We'll see," Fiona said. She was standing next to Philip, her left hand with its bright engagement ring moving up and down his shoulder. "I'm not sure I'm going to feel up to traveling. As you can tell, I'm pretty hormonal."

Sophie looked to her brother.

"Fiona's pregnant," he said.

"Oh, wow," Sophie said. Fiona was staring at her with an expectant smile. "Congratulations," she remembered to say.

"Thank you! We're thrilled," Fiona said, and her stroking of Philip's arm picked up in pace. She was beaming. This was her show; the whole weekend, Sophie thought, had been her show. Even the letter. She thought of her mother on the day the letter came, the way her voice sounded when she said, "I always thought of him, wondering where he was, every minute of every day." Unspoken was the idea that he, too, had been thinking of her, somewhere off in the world.

"I should go," Sophie said.

They offered to take her all the way to the train, but Sophie refused. She wanted to be alone, to plan what she'd tell her mother. *It was as if we'd known each other all our lives.* It was her turn now to leave out everything that couldn't be said. The last thing her brother offered, as she left, was "Keep in touch," as if they were friends from high school whom college choices might force apart. Fiona jumped in: they had friends in Boston, they'd come visit and take Sophie and her roommate out to dinner. Sophie believed this. Fiona would drag Philip to Boston and probably, eventually, to California, showing him everywhere family, everywhere people to whom he was connected.

Indeed, this is what happened. The child was born and named Andrew, and he looked like Sophie and Philip: the same red hair, the same square boxy face. When Fiona brought him to California, she presented him to Sophie's mother like a trophy, and Sophie's mother exclaimed happily over him, and said all the right things, and it wasn't until after the visitors left that she locked herself in the bedroom and cried over everything she had lost: a whole child's future, a whole child's past.

On a drunken Thanksgiving night years in the future, Fiona would confess to Sophie that she wanted to have other children after Andrew, but that Philip was against it; too much money, too much time would be required. "He doesn't understand about family," Fiona would say angrily, this initial grain of opinion having hardened to a sturdy pearl. Sophie, four glasses of wine in her, struggling through divorce, would only nod exhaustedly, too drunk to remember Fiona as a young woman aglow with her child and her confidence and her love. Whether she remembered it or not, though, this was the end of her own childhood: the day she left Fiona and her brother in New York, Fiona waving goodbye with one hand and holding on to Philip with the other, as if without her tethering him he threatened to float away into some other orbit. This escape Fiona would not allow. Instead she would hold his arm and smile at Sophie, her eyes sparkling fervently, amply sparkling, as if she felt so full of love that she could afford to give some away.

Everybody Serves Caesar: Chicago Stories

Alewives

The year the alewives were washing up on the shores of the lake and their stench rose up from the beaches so that even when you couldn't smell them anymore they stank up your memory. Newly dead they were a silvery blue. In the sun they were like hundreds of mirrors. They yellowed as they dried up. And the smell changed, too, from freshly dead to something slightly less pungent but more permanent. A kind of sweet pickled rot. Alewives swim in schools. They died together, as it should be. The tide delivered them up by the bucketful. One beach they needed a dump truck to haul them away. I think of their small dead mouths. What kind of God allows for the massacre of fish that even fishermen spare? The newspapers called them nuisance fish, in life and in death. Non-indigenous to Lake Michigan. Something to do with coming in with ships from the St. Lawrence Seaway. I liked the idea of fish as stowaways. I'd go down to Millard's after school and take off my shoes and walk on them, crack the thin bones of their backs.

Comiskey

for Beaumont

Lou would take us to Sox games at old Comiskey. We'd sit in the left-field bleachers. Lou rarely said a word. All that razzing, bellowing, spitting, guzzling, and he'd watch the pigeons stab the popcorn at his feet. After he died people described his life as having been sad. I'm not sure this is right. Because he hadn't been successful, the family was forever trying to diagnose him. It is true that he always seemed distracted. But it seems to me now that he was probably weighted less by sadness than by his bills. I think those games were a kind of reprieve.

Sometimes he'd turn his head to look at the girls strutting up and down the bleacher steps. These were broiling summer nights in Chicago, and the bleachers were a scantily clad place. Flesh: beer guts and tits all over. But mostly he just watched the pigeons. Only occasionally would he look at the field to make sure everything was going along the way it should. For Lou, the less action the better. A home run, and he'd hardly flinch. These were the Bill Veeck years of the exploding pinwheel scoreboard and the fireworks would be popping off and we'd all be going nuts because everybody else was going nuts and anyway it broke up the monotony. Lou would stand like everybody else, but he'd never hoot or yahoo. He'd sit down long before anybody else and wait for it to return to ordinary. A barely foul ball, a check swing, a 2 and 2 count. To him, I think, it was a game of beautiful almosts. All that yelling had nothing to do with it. It was about possibility, not fruition. If something happens it goes from dream to gone. *Don't you people know this?*

They say he was sad over business troubles. He sold suits for a living, which according to the family was an almost unspeakable tragedy, given his education. They say he was sad over marriage troubles. And Irene was never healthy. Sometime in the early eighties she stopped leaving the house altogether. Whatever it was, he was always kind to us. Lou bought us more hot dogs and doughy pretzels than we knew what to do with. My brother and I would bop each other on the head with our churros. I remember what the light was like at Comiskey, not a total blinding brightness like you see today. Comiskey light was spotty. There were always bulbs that needed to be replaced. The bleachers lived in darkness. If you dropped a quarter under your seat you'd have to grope around like you were at the movies. Amazing some of the things you'd find. A half-eaten candy bar with a label you wouldn't recognize. A petrified roach. A cake of snot from the 1920's. And from within that darkness, we watched the light. Dust particles were visible in the streams that separated us from the rest of the park like a shroud.

After the game he'd comment on the score out of obligation, the dirty white colossus rising behind us as we walked across the parking lot. They tore Comiskey down. Here, they tear everything down eventually. He never mentioned any current players' names. Richie Zisk and Dick Allen meant nothing to him. The only player he seemed to know was Swede Risberg. He said if Risberg had been paid enough in the first place he'd never have been tempted. Blame a man for only wanting his due? Another thing the family used to say about Lou was that he was a non-practicing socialist. Poor loser, they said, the man never made enough to implement his noble ideas.

Lou also had no sense of direction. He always lost the car. As we wandered the rows, he'd ask us, so gorged on food we were bloated to the eyeballs, if we had enough to eat.

"You're sure now?"

He died too young, broke. Men tend to disappoint early in my family. There were no children. They sent Irene to Florida to live with her sister. I rarely think of him. I thought of him today. I can't say why. It's December, and there's no baseball. Maybe it is only the blue dark of this lingering afternoon. He was my mother's brother. Since he knew my father thought baseball was a waste of time, maybe Lou felt we needed someone to take us to games. We never had the heart to tell him we didn't care either way. I've come to see, though, that it was less about us than him. That he must have been grateful to us for giving him an excuse. He must have known our excitement over home runs was a sham to make the night go quicker. For Lou it never went slow enough.

My Parents Listening to Dionne Warwick

June 1973

They don't speak. Their marriage, such as it was, is nearly over, though officially it will continue another four years. Soon my mother will begin sleeping in the guest room behind a deadbolt. But tonight all is quiet and they sit listening to Dionne on the stereo and these days are getting longer and these nights are lasting decades and my mother puts her hand slowly to her mouth and breathes into her fingers. Between them, on the low table, is a chessboard, my father's. My mother doesn't play. The light outside is greenish, a kind of reflection of the lawn which stretches all the way to the street. The people who owned this house before us left a tall flagpole on the lawn. When I was six, while playing running bases with Jerry Lemieux, I ran into the flagpole and conked myself out. Another time, I threw the ball to Jerry and it hit him in the mouth and he lost his two front teeth. Does a lawn retain its histories? Do chairs? Living rooms? Locked doors? My father watches the flagpole. He no longer hoists the flag every morning but the rope that runs the flag up the pole remains and so does the heavy metal clasp which continues even on a night with so little wind to clang like a halyard against a mast, a faraway sound my mother likes. What's it all about when you sort it out, Alfie? My mother looks at the chessboard. My father coughs, but he doesn't say anything. He won't try to touch her tonight. She looks up, not at him, past him, at the wall behind his head where she had always meant to hang something.

A Visit to the Judge

He was a great man, a learned man. In the words of one West Side precinct captain, "The yid really classed up the joint."

A federal judge! Think, my boy, of the heights you yourself might one day rise!

This is the truth, as best as I can remember. It's an attempt to make Jell-O of a moment, to preserve for good how it was when as a Jewish kid from Chicago you'd sit for the first time in one of those big, squishy leather chairs in Abraham Lincoln Marovitz's chambers and listen to him tell you what it meant to be a man, an American, above all a Chicagoan. My brother once presented the judge with a drawing of himself and his namesake. In the picture the two of them are sitting on a bench talking politics. The caption beneath their feet reads: *Just a Couple of Abes.* Marovitz got a big kick out of that. "Just," he roared. "Just!"

In the index of Mike Royko's *Boss*, the judge is listed like this:

Marovitz, Abraham Lincoln, 41–46; and Mafia, 42; association with underworld figures 42–43; influenced by "friendships," 43–44; friendship with Richard Daley 44–45; preoccupation with Abe Lincoln, 41–42.

Now, I have no truck with Royko's insinuations. I'm a Jewish kid from Chicago, and I remain a loyal, if wayward, stalwart. And hey, if he was crooked he wasn't that crooked, which in Chicago, as everywhere, if everywhere was as honest about being dishonest, means something.

So it was a rite of passage to be taken by your father to the judge's chambers for a chat. In some families, mine included, you didn't get bar mitzvahed. To leave childhood behind, you went to see Judge Marovitz.

It wasn't a chat. You sat there, swallowed up in one of those enormous chairs, afraid to even move because of how loud the crinkle would sound in your ears, and you listened. But let me take a step back... Before you listened, you waited, and in that waiting was a silence so absolute it was drowning in the lake, out past that point where the sandbar gave way to blue emptiness. You alone, your father in the judge's anteroom, pacing. And the old judge staring at you, staring, staring. His head was nothing special, but the thicket of his single eyebrow made him royal. His face and ears and bald pate were ruddy as befitted a man who kept his chambers heartily cold. And his hands clasped before him, abnormally still for an old man. He was, people said, statuesque. But his eyes beneath the thicket were full of motion, and to meet them straight on (as you were told by your father to do) caused a churn in your stomach. And above him, as if to enforce the power of his gaze a hundred-fold, an armada of images of Lincoln. Paintings, photographs, etchings, silhouettes, drawings by boys like your brother. And on the tables, busts of Lincoln. And they'd all be watching you, too—this was a test—and the silence was only broken by the judge's sporadic wheezing. The fourteenth floor of the Federal Building. After-hours, February. Then, as if to reach a branch out to a sinking you, the judge would slowly raise one hand and wave it to encompass the surrounding presidents who were all the same president, and with the index finger of his other hand he'd point to a framed picture on his desk of his parents. Black and white, lined faces, hollow-eyed peasants from Lithuania. The judge looked a bit like a traffic cop exhorting you to look one way and then another, but you'd get it. You were prepared by your father to get it. You were given to understand the miracle that was this country, this city. From a

Kentucky log cabin to the White House! From a Lithuanian shtetl to the U.S. Courthouse! Look at him. Look at them. Look at me. My father was a peddler. My mother sewed buttons for the landowner's wife. And then he'd tell another oft-repeated legend. How his mother first got wind of the great emancipator at a meeting of socialists in Podberzeya. How she heard that after he freed the slaves, Lincoln got shot in the temple. In the head, Mother, it means in the head! Nothing could convince my mother that Lincoln wasn't a Jew! And the two of you would laugh, but the judge would stop laughing earlier and so your laugh would hang there alone, between you, like an insult. And the judge's ruddy face would droop then, become sad. Sad because there were some boys, there were always some boys, who failed to embrace the opportunity that was being handed to them on the silverest of all platters. Maybe you yourself were one of those boys who would squander God's gift of Chicago. One of those boys who would take the gift for granted...

Not that any gift worth salt comes without a price. Remember this for all time. But my God, here we are free to live. To live! No czars, no Cossacks, no Stalins. Here we answer only to the Constitution! With, note, an unwritten stipulation. Some call it patronage, I call it friendship. Nobody is his own man. Everybody needs somebody else. Just as in the old country, everybody serves Caesar, understand? The difference is: here you get a shot at playing Caesar in the movie. And so does your neighbor. And your neighbor's cousin Alben. We scratch each other's backs in this city. I scratch you. You scratch me. Nice to have your back scratched. Especially those places you can't reach. This is how we build our buildings tallest of the tall. Our highways, fourteen lanes across. Sears, Roebuck, Marshall Fields, Wiebolt's, Goldblatt's, Carson, Pierre, Scott. Back scratchers all. Do you think we could have reversed the flow of the Chicago River? This kind of engineering marvel if not for the scratch, scratch, scratching of one another's backs?

The judge would sneeze then, an internal, handless sneeze, the sneeze of a man for whom sneezes were not an obstacle to straight dope.

And it wasn't absurd. If it sounds absurd it is memory's fault and not the judge's. Thank God he's in a place he can't see me now, a postcard squanderer. What I'm trying to say is that it was a show, a show you studied for, a show you rehearsed for, but there was something fundamental about it that wasn't a show at all. You can laugh when you remember all those sorrowful Lincolns staring at you from all directions, but the longer you sat in that chair in your cold feet, the more you began to see what this whole ordeal was really about. Because it was less his words, less all the back scratching, than the incoming darkness, the gray doomful light that was settling over that room through the half-closed blinds. You were being told in no uncertain terms: Don't be cute. Your flesh will wither up, too. Don't be cowed into the old hood-wink that you've got your whole life ahead of you. Even cows aren't so stupid. Do they ever stop eating the grass that's in front of them? And then the old judge would swoop a breath and laugh. He'd really laugh. A terrible, high-pitched, squinty laugh. His eyes would disappear beneath his brows. The skin around his skull would seem to tighten, and all at once his cherry ruddy face would go pale—dead.

And so would you seem dead in the winter Chicago light.

Relieved, though, too. Because you'd been prepared for this also. *Make it past the laugh. All you have to do is make it past the laugh, and you're home free.*

He'd reach then to his shelf and pull out the scriptures. He'd leaf, seemingly at random, until he came to his favorite book, Numbers. Then intone: "And all the congregation lifted up their voice and cried; and the people wept that night. And all the children of Israel murmured against Moses and against Aaron; and the whole congregation said unto them: 'Would that we had died in the land of Egypt.'"

Slapping the book shut, the judge would lean toward you, over the great desk, and begin the quiz: "How did Moses respond to this cowardice and ingratitude?"

"First he put his head in the sand, your Honor."

"And then?"

"He pleaded with the people, your Honor."

"And then?"

"The people still wouldn't listen."

"Yes! And then?"

"Well, they stoned him, your Honor."

"Lesson?"

"Accept to be stoned."

"Accept to be stoned for what?"

"For the greater glory, your Honor."

"Right. True. And on a more practical level?"

"The stoning hastened the arrival of God to his rescue, which meant—after a minor plague for punishment—they could get a move on again. Wandering gets tiresome, your Honor. Moses wanted to get to the promised land already."

"Sustained! And did he reach the promised land?"

And you'd pause. Weigh your answer with the heavy burden of study, of knowledge, of the sad irony of it: "No, your Honor, he never did. In the end, he, too, disobeyed God and—"

"Yes. *And*?"

"He died alone. No family. No friends."

"Lesson?"

"Stay on the right side of Caesar." Forget Moses. Goodbye, Abe. Your days are done. You were good stories, good men. This, my friend, is Chicago, 1975. Nobody goes it alone anymore, ever.

The skull would nod. Gradually, you'd be clapped for. The judge's little hands in slow syncopation, clap, clap, clap. The room all shadows now. For a while you'd sit together in the dark until it was time for him to ring the little bell. Tinkle, tinkle. Then, at last, his secretary would enter—the light draining into the room as if from another world—and she'd take you by the arm and tow you out to where your proud father would be waiting with his hat in hands.

The Collage

Once more into that house on Detamble, through the basement door. There it still is. Along the wall beside the basement stairs. The huge, framed collage my grandmother made for my grandfather on the occasion of his sixtieth birthday. Newspaper clippings, postcards, war dispatches, telegrams.

DARLING BERNICE. REACHED NEW GEORGIA. ONE PIECE. BRAIN SCRAMBLED EGGS. WAR NOT CAKE. ONLY EATABLE CAKE IS YOU.

—SEYMOUR

And in the center of it all, a photograph of my grandfather in his smart naval officer's uniform. Below him a quote: *In the naval service, there are customs and usages that are peculiar to the personnel serving in the navy. The origin of many of these is obscure, but they have the power of full authority and are conscientiously observed.* Ringing my grandfather's head like a halo are snapshot cutouts of the heads of his loyal crew, his family.

And along the right margin of the collage: DON'T GIVE UP THE SHIP!!!

This is the story. My aunt Esther, at some point in the 1980's, after her divorce, after she'd moved back home and taken over the maid's room in the basement, scratched out the face of her ex-husband on my grandfather's birthday collage. Not such a strange thing. You hear of all kinds of things done to photographs in families. No need for me to say that the pictures we keep in the backs of drawers are frozen lies. Who doesn't want to rid themselves of those mocking faces? But maybe it was the fact that my ex-uncle's face was part of a larger whole that made his obliteration so fascinating to me. The rest of us were all there smiling patriotically around my grandfather's bulbous head. I think it was the proximity of my own intact face to Lloyd's former face that kept me going down the basement stairs to look. I'd survived the onslaught. Because my aunt had scratched his face hard. Of course she had her reasons, good ones, but when I say scratched, I mean hacked. Esther hacked that face so hard there was a hole in the wall behind the collage. I know this because I once took the frame off the wall and looked.

And who could blame her for not wanting to look at that face every time she went up and down the stairs?

I was down there, the collage off the wall, my finger in the hole. My grandmother opened the door and stood at the top of the stairs.

"What are you doing?"

"I wanted to look at the hole."

"What hole?"

"The hole she made when she scratched out Lloyd."

"What?"

She was lying. We'd all seen it and pretended we hadn't. The basement stairs were well-traveled. The laundry was down there, and so was the ping-pong table. Nobody didn't pause to look at that collage. It was a physical reminder of who we were (or used to be), constellations around the planet of my grandfather.

My grandmother standing at the top of the stairs with the June light behind her outlining her body, almost like snow—lying. She breathed a sigh, but held it in her shoulders. Her mouth didn't open, and she stood there and thought of her daughter. Esther was at work then. Through it all—the being back home, the hardly talking to her parents, the cutting herself off from her friends, the untrue rumors of her insanity circling around the country club. *Such a smart sassy beautiful girl, to think. Did you hear? She sleeps in the basement?* Through all that she went to work in an office. And this was almost more humiliation than my grandmother could take. Esther, a receptionist? All those hopes. Say what you want about hopes, that when people yearn for things for other people they are really yearning for themselves. Even so, isn't it a kind of love? Isn't all love warped in one way or another? She wanted things for Esther so she could talk about them, but she also wanted them to be real— for Esther. So forgive her. My grandmother at the top of the basement stairs, mourning not a death, but a life. A daughter who isn't ashamed, who could give a damn what people are saying about her. Who left a rich husband in the dust. Who eats TV dinners in her room with the light off. Love for a daughter at its most fierce and me down there with the collage off the wall and my finger—

I wanted to feel rage in the silence of that house.

Is it possible to go back to a moment when my grandmother and I watched each other? The old house on Detamble? Me halfway down the stairs, her at the top with the door open and the June light? Love trapped in her shoulders?

"Put that back on the wall," she said.

Grand Pacific Hotel, 1875

One hotel maid said her screeching was like the sound of a peacock. But what finally frightened the maids the most was her silence. She'd roam the halls of the hotel as if looking for something in all those halls that looked identical to everyone but her. To her the halls changed every time she wandered down them. Think of the air alone. Morning light like the soot seeps through the dirty windows. At night, blue flames roam the wallppaper. Even she changed—moment by moment—and this is why there are no safe harbors anywhere. Even you people who understand nothing must understand this. This hall, that hall. *Come to me, Father, oh, come to Molly, Father.* Because don't you see? Movement is where loss is. If one could only be still. But then how to search? How to find?

Then came a time when she couldn't take another step, and the corridors mazed around her mind, now straight, now twisting. She leaves his side of the bed free. People think he never sleeps. They think he stands vigil all night over the corpses. If they knew. He sleeps. He sleeps with his mouth open and drools like a child.

I am the one who does not sleep.

Once, she tugged the pillow out from under her head and held it in front of her with both hands and looked at it. Then she asked the maid, wonder in her tone, "What's this cruel thing for, Helen?"

The girl stood there and gaped.

Light as a Feather

Mackey Conlon didn't believe in God or science. She believed in patterns in the world you had to be sharp enough to catch. Feelings you had to be open enough to feel. She wasn't one of those crunchy freaks; she just believed in the ability to see things for yourself. Who else was going to watch out for you? So when, on the Sunday night four days before Christmas, a warm front invaded and hailstones began to pelt the house, she saw it as a sign. Her husband, Taylor, told her it was nothing, just hail. Need he remind her that they lived on a big mountain in Vermont?

Taylor was a lawyer. He talked like that. She tried not to hold it against him.

It was nine-thirty. She went to the window. Some of the hailstones were the size of peas, some of jacks' balls. They bounced off the icy snow. In the winter, you could see across the backfield to Sam and Patty Coe's place. They had two sets of twins. The hail stopped midway across the field.

She tapped the glass to get Taylor's attention. "*They're* not getting hailed on," she said.

She tried not to envy the Coes their abundant family, but every time she brought them up, she could feel Taylor steeling himself, readying his arguments about their own blessings. One side of his family was Quaker. He believed in blessings and everyone getting their say. When he had something really important to talk to her about, he stood up, as if in a meetinghouse.

He joined her at the window. "Huh," he said. "Weird." He said it like he didn't think it was weird at all. His last name was Whittredge. His family's primary value was taking things in stride. There wasn't a problem that couldn't be handled. All the men in his family sounded like they'd been named after dogs. There were no men in her family.

The baby kicked, as if reminding her that she should talk: Mackey was a ridiculous name, a nickname from a women's rugby league in high school. It had to do with the force of her tackles. Her real name was Edith. She didn't like it, either.

Most days, ever since sailing through the first trimester, she felt ungenerous and petty. She'd said something about it to her mother once, and her mother had said, "What do you expect? Six miscarriages in four years. Fake baby-making scientific hooha. How else are you supposed to feel?"

Her mother's comment had done what her comments always did: made her want to curl up in her mother's lap and hang up on her at the same time. She could always be counted on to ratify the way Mackey was secretly feeling about herself, but four years of marriage and therapy were beginning to teach her daughter that maybe she deserved to believe in something more than, or different from, herself.

Taylor was banging around the kitchen, hunting for candles, "just in case." "Eureka," he said quietly to himself, and Mackey heard the matches shake in their box and then watched him walk back to her like an altar boy. Once when he'd been renovating the house, he'd been downstairs installing the bathroom floor. He'd thought he was alone, but she'd been upstairs, lying on the bed, listening to him work. She'd heard a terrific crash, and she'd sat up, ready to call out. And then she'd heard him imitating the static of a loudspeaker. "Houston," he said. "We have a problem."

Now on days when she looked at him, unable to understand how they were going to negotiate a life together, she brought out that moment, and fell in love with him again.

"Ssh," she said.

The moon lit the driveway and yard. In the big oak, an owl. Its head was swiveled to the left, as if making a point of ignoring her.

The baby was arching and twisting like a toddler having a tantrum. Her due date was eight days away.

"I know," she said softly, to her belly. "I see it."

Taylor was next to her. "Hey," he said, "an owl."

"Ssh," she said.

"He can't hear us," he said.

"Of course he can," she said.

"He's beautiful," he said.

"He's a sign of death," she said.

Taylor seemed genuinely perplexed. "Owls?" he said. "Really? Where'd you read that?"

She was crying. "Reading isn't the only way to *know* things," she said. "I just know it."

She didn't have to confirm his expression. She'd been crying a lot the last few months. He'd told her that she deserved this baby and this life. She believed that he believed that about her, and it moved her. *He* moved her. But she didn't believe it herself. And here was a hailstorm and an owl to tell her she'd been right all along. A life like this was possible, but not for her.

The next morning the hail and the owl were gone.

"See?" Taylor said. "Nothing to worry about."

She tried to let herself be calmed. She pushed her big belly gently from one side and then the other.

"The baby's not moving," she said.

Taylor was in the bathroom, running the shower. "Sleeping," he said. "Resting up for the big day."

She heard the shower curtain open and close. She watched the steam around the open door. She realized with surprise that quickly turned to guilt and fear that she'd slept through the whole night. She hadn't had an entire night's sleep in the last two months, the baby working her womb like someone making pizza.

She lay very still. Sometimes that worked. Nothing. She called the doctor. He told her it was probably nothing, but if she was worried, if it would make her feel better, she should just come on in for an ultrasound. "We're here to make you feel better," he said.

She did not want to feel better. She'd lost six babies. She'd gone through the first trimester on tiptoe. Her lip had a raw spot on it from her picking at it. Even into the second and the third trimesters, she hadn't been able to celebrate. Life with her mother had taught her that when things looked good it was only because they were about to get bad.

She'd been in the exam room only three days ago. She tried to be reassured by the routine. Shirt up. Cold goop. Ultrasound slipping around on her belly.

There was her baby, perfect and curled. A girl. When you did as many procedures as they'd done, you knew more than you'd ever thought possible about someone who hadn't yet entered the world. They'd named her months ago, but hadn't told anyone.

Taylor squeezed her hand.

The doctor moved the ultrasound around. And then he stopped. He held her wrist, and when she looked up at him, she knew.

She'd met her husband at the public library in Bath, Maine. He was staying at his family's summerhouse—the cottage, they called the place she'd always thought was a hotel—and studying for the bar. She was living in the town where she'd always lived, working at the library, trying to stay out of the way of an ex-boyfriend and practicing treating her body like a temple. She hadn't had a drink or a drug in three months when Taylor piled a stack of books in front of her, his childhood library card in his hand.

They'd met again at the bar. Her bartending job was a test. If she could stay sober there, she was home free.

He'd been dragged in by some friends. They had the giddy look of boys being bad. The other bartender rolled his eyes at her. She rolled hers back. The townie-girl/summer-boy romance was a joke. Even her mother had given up on that get-ahead plan.

One of the friends had lined up shot after shot of Cuervo Gold for him. Another had gotten her number for him. She still didn't know why she'd given it.

He called two days later. It was eleven in the morning, and she was asleep. She'd heard voices in the background, and then a door closing, and then nothing. And then he'd asked her out in what she'd learn was the slow, careful way he did everything. He'd never slept with anyone else in his entire life. She'd found that out at the reproductive clinic when they'd both had to fill out a fertility history. She repeated it to herself, sometimes out loud.

And then he'd passed the bar, and gotten the right kind of job representing people like her, in Vermont, and asked her to come with him, and she had, working on her photography, finding a job as an art teacher at a local private school.

Their story bored her. Their infertility bored her. It was the same as a million other people's, some of whom she'd met in waiting rooms, all of them eyeing each other, as if there were only so many babies and the criteria for getting one hadn't been made clear.

There'd been only one surprise along the way. They'd tried "on their own" *to no avail*—Taylor's language again. And then they'd gone to Dr. Breedlove. "Doctor *Breedlove?*" her mother had said. But to Mackey, he was just a guy from the South who'd given her friend Ginny triplets, and Sue from the store twins, and Priscilla at the bank a single on the way. She didn't care about his name. Somewhere there was a room filled with healthy babies, and he had the key.

So there'd been tests for both of them. They'd gone to the office for the results. Mackey had thought of it as the Laying-of-Blame visit. Your ovaries are shriveled, your fallopian tubes death traps: what made you think you deserved a baby?

She'd said, sitting there, "Her womb was a rocky place where his seed could find no purchase."

Taylor had put a hand on her shoulder. He'd never seen *Raising Arizona*. She'd watched it after every miscarriage, curled up on the couch in the middle of the night, the volume down low.

He palmed the back of her head with his big hand. If he'd been born a different race and class, he'd have been a basketball player, seven children with six different women.

They already knew she had scar tissue from some fallopian fibroids she'd had removed. But Taylor, it turned out, had what Dr. Breedlove called "challenged swimmers." Sperm had to work hard; some of them weren't up to the job.

"Huh," Taylor had said.

There was a procedure they could try. It might work.

"Might?" Mackey had asked.

Dr. Breedlove had looked her way as if having to remind himself she was in the room. "Sorry. You're right. Let's stay positive here. That's half the battle. *Will* work."

Staying positive hadn't been what she had in mind. She didn't care anything about happy prayers or homeopathic charms. She wanted to walk down Main Street pushing a stroller, a baby tucked inside.

On the way home, Taylor had kept saying he couldn't believe it until Mackey had started to feel insulted.

"What's your thrust here?" she said. "You're shocked it was you instead of me? You just couldn't imagine a problem coming from somewhere other than your recovering addict wife?"

He stared at her. "I don't know what you're talking about," he said.

She didn't, either. Where did these things come from?

She thought about how to apologize.

"It's not really about you," he said.

"I know," she said.

"Okay, then," he said.

He held the steering wheel at ten and two, his shoulders up around his ears, hunching even more than usual.

She put her head in his lap. He was wearing work boots. When he got home, he would split wood. She had a lawyer husband who stacked wood and built his own house. How had that happened to her? Why wasn't she more grateful?

"Sorry," she'd said into his thigh.

He'd put his hand on her hip. "It's okay," he'd said.

He was a good person. If the procedure didn't work, if there were no babies, he would be the strong one. He would take care of her.

They checked into the hospital they'd toured months before. They saw the same nurses, though this time there was no joking and teasing, no general sense of the goodness of life. Everyone was super-efficient, as if Mackey and Taylor were hospital inspectors here to catalogue flaws.

An IV was begun, a bag of saline and another of Pitocin to start her labor. She was hooked to a monitor. Down the hall, a woman cried out.

She looked up at the nurse. "How long is this going to take?" she asked.

The nurse wrapped a warm hand around her ankle. "Can't really predict," she said. "Just like a regular delivery."

After an epidural and hours of contractions she couldn't feel, she was awake. "We've made a mistake," she said.

Taylor was sitting in a scoop chair next to her. "What, sweetie?" he asked.

"She's alive," she said.

He stood and put his palm to her forehead. "She's not," he said.

She took his hand and held it against her belly. "I *feel* her," she said.

He rested his head against hers. "Whatever you feel, it isn't her," he said.

His parents had paid for it all. Dr. Breedlove had explained chromosome paints and shown them pictures, a long probe puncturing her egg like she'd once seen a magician's needle puncture a balloon.

When she'd been a child, her mother had thrown a Halloween party where Mackey had been It for a game of Stiff as a Board, Light as a Feather. The feeling of being lifted off the ground by her mother's fingers had made her dizzy with pleasure.

Nora Louise was born on Tuesday, December 24th. Six pounds, seven ounces. Twenty-one inches long. Perfect, with her father's long torso and her mother's stubby toes.

The nurses cleaned her off, swaddled her, and handed her to Mackey. "You take as long as you need," she said to both of them. She stood there for a minute, all of them looking down at Nora, still and quiet in her white flannel hospital blanket.

Years from now, she would still be here, in this bed, holding her baby girl.

The nurse wiped at her eyes. "You call me when you're ready," she said, touching both of them lightly on their arms.

Two normal embryos had been implanted: one stayed, growing and growing. There'd been celebratory calls and visits from Taylor's family. Even Mackey's mother had been happy for them, though she'd turned down an invitation to visit, saying she had too much going on. In the background, Mackey heard the latest New Friend changing channels.

"Come on," Mackey had said. "You can see me pregnant."

"Oh, Mackey," her mother said. "I've seen that before." And Mackey's hope that a baby would make everything better had started to give just a little.

"What do you think she'll be like?" Taylor had taken to asking, late at night or early in the morning, lying in bed, circling her belly button with his finger.

Mackey always shrugged, not wanting to admit that she hadn't thought about that at all. Instead she'd marveled at the changes she herself was undergoing. Not just shape and size, but a kind of narrowing of vision. As if pregnancy was the equivalent of giving up photography for miniature painting. She imagined the world sharing her new focus, as if she'd been put in the middle of a wide stage, a spotlight picking her out from the chorus.

Now, holding her dead baby, she couldn't imagine what she'd found compelling about herself. She felt like hanging a sign, warning others away.

They dressed her in the jumper and cardigan that Taylor's sister had knitted. Purple, the color of Maine sunsets, his sister had said, but now all Mackey saw was bruise.

"Take her out of it," she said. "It's ugly."

"Okay," Taylor said. He undressed her and laid her on the bed. He searched through the duffel he'd brought and came out with an old-fashioned dress that they'd found at the Goodwill. He cradled Nora's head, pulling the dress over it. He helped one arm, then the other, into the tiny cap sleeves. The pinks of the dress reflected off her pale skin, like she'd spent the day in a brisk wind.

Both of them were crying. Mackey imagined going on and doing the things she'd always done, and she could, but only if she imagined herself sobbing the entire way.

She pulled her camera from the duffel and began shooting. Taylor cradled Nora in his arms, smoothing the dress out over her tiny feet, her still-tucked-up legs.

She wanted evidence that this girl had been here. That she'd been known.

Christmas came and went. Taylor took time off from work. They did what they had to do. They fed the dog, watered the plants, ate what they could of the platters and pans from friends and neighbors that filled the fridge. They peed, they slept.

The phone never stopped ringing. She let it ring. Taylor answered it. From her bed, she heard him telling the story in his low voice to people who genuinely cared, but whose faces she wanted to slap. But even anger required too much energy. Life went on, every moment of it an affront.

Her mother called, and Mackey told her not to come. It wasn't necessary. There was nothing to do.

His parents came instead. After them, his sister, then his brother, both without their children. They cleaned and cooked. Taylor went for long runs, happy, she was sure, to have someone else around to babysit her.

Should we come again? they all asked. What would be best?

It doesn't matter, she told them. And it didn't.

The doctor gave them both medications. To help with sleep. To take the edge off. The childproof bottles stayed unopened, lined up on the dresser.

She didn't go into the nursery.

More snow fell. Temperatures dropped. Taylor built large, excessive fires in the woodstove. The heat was a weight on her chest. They walked around the house in their underwear. They didn't touch each other. Three weeks passed.

The call came from her mother's neighbor: her mother had been found wandering on the frozen pond in her nightie. Five in the morning. "I don't know if you keep up with our weather," the neighbor said, "but it's mighty cold up here at five in the morning."

She had a mild case of frostbite on her toes and fingers. She was in the hospital in Portland.

Mackey wasn't sure what was being asked of her, if anything. She and her mother hadn't taken care of each other in years, maybe ever. She tried to make her thick tongue formulate appropriate questions.

"Does she want me to call her?" she asked. The first time her mother had gone into the hospital, when Mackey was eight, to have, Mackey later found out, an abortion, her mother hadn't told her where she was going, just that she had to be in the hospital for what shouldn't be longer than a day or so and not to worry. Her mother had always presented worrisome situations and then told her not to worry.

The neighbor seemed as confused as Mackey, but for different reasons. "I think, dear, she's confused about what she wants." She gave Mackey the number at the hospital and the name of the attending, and asked if Mackey wanted her to water her mother's plants.

How had Mackey been put in charge of her mother's plants? "Where's Hank?" she asked.

The neighbor cleared her throat. "He hasn't been around in quite some time now."

Mackey pondered the news. Other lives were going on all around her. She thanked the woman and told her yes, please, water the plants, and anything else she could think of. She hung up and sat staring at the phone.

Taylor came in from outside, an armful of wood up to his neck. He slammed the door with his foot and began filling the rack next to the stove.

She watched him. When he was done, he stood up, brushing wood crumbs from the front of his shirt. He looked at her. "What?"

"I think my mom's going to have to come stay here for a while," she said.

"Okay," he said, simple and without a second thought.

Without discussing it, they gave her the nursery. Taylor dismantled the crib and the changing table, bungee-cording the pieces together, saving the screws and brackets in Ziploc bags duct-taped to the ends of the crib.

Mackey painted the moss green a bright yellow that was more Piece-of-Work-Mother, less Tiny New Person. She took down the curtains and mobiles, emptied drawers, and replaced little hangers with adult-sized ones. She left the large black and white photograph she'd taken of herself and Taylor. Her mother should feel welcome, part of something.

When they were done, they sat on the couch watching the news with the sound off.

Her mother turned out to be a different person: no longer the self-sufficient narcissist; now an anxious, fluttery, completely dependent narcissist. Mackey had no idea what to make of her.

The first night didn't go well. Her mother didn't sleep, wandering the house, stumbling into unfamiliar furniture, testing locked doors, muttering. It didn't matter; Mackey wasn't sleeping, either. She got in and out of bed and took her mother back to her room, using the same route each time, hoping to imprint some kind of inner map-making ability. Penelope, the dog, stopped getting up.

"I can't stay here," her mother kept saying. "Take me back."

"Sure you can," Mackey would answer, leading her back down the hall.

At five in the morning, Mackey found her tapping lightly on the inside of the kitchen door. The pockets of her robe were pretty seriously stuffed with sugar packets. Mackey wrapped her in a wool throw. Her mother shrugged it off.

"I've got to get out of here," she said.

Mackey stood with her, looking out the half-window in the door. The snow was a sickly blue. The wind that had been going all night was gone. Nothing moved.

"Where do you want to go?" she asked.

"Where do you think?" her mother said. She grabbed Mackey's forearm with both hands.

Mackey couldn't look at her. She looked out past the snowy field to the snowy woods, and past that to the sky. She imagined them opening the door and making their escape, running across the hard snow like girls.

She tried the wool throw on her mother's shoulders again. A lifetime of drinking and smoking had turned her body into something sharp and hard. Mackey rubbed her arms. "This is home," she said.

Her mother asked her if she remembered the time she didn't want to take a bath. Mackey knew the reference. She'd been ten. She didn't remember why she hadn't wanted to bathe. They'd been visiting someone with a beach house her mother was trying to date. Her mother had dragged her down the hallway by both arms. Mackey had knocked paintings and pictures off the walls.

Now her mother patted her robe pockets, looking for cigarettes. "Whose house was that?" she asked. "That was a nice place."

Mackey led her to the table and pulled a chair out for her. She opened a bottom drawer and dug around, coming up with a pack of cigarettes she'd hidden years ago. She lit one for her mother, and then one for herself.

"Frank Moody," she said.

"I think you're right," her mother said, exhaling. "Frank Moody," she repeated, watching the smoke curl up out of her mouth.

And for the next two weeks sometimes her mother was there and sometimes she wasn't. Sometimes, Mackey and Taylor woke to the smell of eggs and bacon and fresh biscuits, the table set.

Sometimes, they woke to the door wide open, her mother in the car, trying to start it with the house key.

Most days were days of ordinary flatness. They did jigsaw puzzles and crosswords, her mother pretending to help with both. Taylor shoveled the walk, the two women scattering salt behind him. Her mother leafed through the newspaper. Mackey clipped her mother's finger- and toenails, rubbing lotion into her hands and feet. She filled the humidifiers. Her mother watered the plants and talked to the dog. She cooked meals Mackey had no idea she knew how to make. She cleaned the venetian blinds in the bathroom, one slat at a time. At the grocery she got in a fight with the man at the deli counter. She said afterwards that she knew what kind of person he was.

And driving home, Mackey understood that the flatness wasn't ordinary, it was a heavy weight, a cast-iron lid, trying to hold everything down.

Once she was digging small holes in the snow with the heel of her slipper halfway across the field. Taylor pulled his boots on and trudged out to get her.

Two weeks into that, he took Mackey aside in the kitchen. "We can't live like this forever," he said.

All the way through elementary school, when the bus got to her stop, someone would say, "You *live* here?"

"Like what?" Mackey asked.

He looked around like the answer was in the kitchen. "She can't be happy," he said. He paused like he'd forgotten what he was talking about. "We need help," he finally said.

"Then *do* something," she said.

The night before the autopsy results were due back, her mother had wanted to give her a makeover.

Taylor had gone to bed hours before; any kind of anxiety always made him sleepy. Mackey knew she'd be up for hours. "I don't think so," she told her mom.

Her mother had her red fake leather case open on the kitchen table, its trays expanded like bleachers. It looked like a model of a football stadium. "Tools of the trade," she'd said when Mackey looked through it as a girl.

"Come on," her mother said. "I'll do your face. We'll paint each other's nails. You can watch bad TV."

"Bad TV is bad for you," Mackey said.

Her mother was lining up bottles of polish. She gave one a hard shake and frowned at her daughter. "How did I get a daughter like you?" she asked. "Sometimes I wonder."

"That makes two of us," Mackey said.

"I'm sure it does," her mother said. She regarded her daughter. "To be honest," she said, "your face could use some doing."

"Mom," Mackey said. "If we were going to list each other's problems..."

Her mother held a hand up. "Don't get mad. I'm just being a friend, telling the truth." She dug around in her box. "Nothing I can't fix," she said.

Her mother liked to sum up her maternal philosophy every so often by saying, I'm your friend, not your mother. She didn't believe in behavior based on genetic responsibility. She believed in free will. Whatever she did, she did because she wanted to. Mackey shouldn't expect anything else.

For a long time, Mackey had thought it was a liberated way to think.

This time it seemed important not to let it pass. This time, Mackey said, "I don't need a friend. I don't want to be friends with you."

Her mother kept on at it, though. "Don't be ridiculous," she said. "Of course you do."

The next day they got the autopsy results: a compromised connection between umbilical cord and placenta, a freak occurrence, nothing to do with their previous miscarriages, nothing to indicate that the next baby would be anything but healthy.

"I wish I'd had a reason to do a C-section," Dr. Breedlove said. "She would've been fine."

Mackey by that point was a balloon inflated and deflated too many times. She didn't even note the cruelty of his comment. That would be for friends to point out later. She thought of a frayed end of her umbilical cord, all that life leaking out around it, surrounding Nora, useless and unreachable. Had she starved to death? Had all that movement she'd felt the night before been her daughter in agony?

Back home, her mother had emptied the contents of the fridge and the freezer and stacked everything against the wall in her room. She was sleeping on her back in her bed, her mouth open. She was snoring softly. Since she'd been here, she hadn't talked about Nora once.

Taylor returned all the food to its proper place and went for a run. He was training for a marathon. Taylor, silly Taylor.

Mackey went to the kitchen table and stared at the sandwich he'd left her. Penelope lumbered in. Mackey held the sandwich out on the flat of her hand like she was feeding a horse.

The owl was back. In the middle of the day. The sun on the snow was painful. He was on the same branch as before, but this time he was looking straight at her. He stayed like that for forty-five minutes, never taking his big yellow eyes off her. Then he spread his wings and headed right for her, veering up and over the roof at the last minute.

She didn't want reasonable explanations. It was the middle of a sunny day. The same owl. He'd stared at her for forty-five minutes. She turned these facts over and over. She didn't know what to believe; then she did. That owl had been Nora, there to give her something. She just didn't know what.

When her mother woke up, Mackey led her downstairs to the darkroom. "Keep me company," she said. Taylor had surprised her by converting the back room for their first anniversary.

She settled her mom in a chair and took out the roll of film of Nora.

"It's very dirty," her mother said. Her face these last weeks had softened. It was like dough dusted with flour.

Mackey shrugged and kept at her work. She hadn't been in here in months, afraid of what the chemicals could do to the baby.

Her mother looked around, suddenly anxious. "Where are we?"

"We're here, in the darkroom, in the house, in Burlington, Vermont, in the United States of America," Mackey said.

Her mother wasn't reassured. Mackey supposed she was right not to be. Upstairs, Taylor's footsteps, the paired thumps of his sneakers being tossed into the corner.

"We're just here," Mackey said. "Here is safe. Come on."

Her mother joined her at the table, the three white enamel trays in a row in front of them.

The first image began to appear. The pattern of the dress, the curled fingers.

Her mother held her hand to her mouth. "Oh!" she said. "What a thing. How on earth did you do that?" she asked.

"It's just chemicals," Mackey said, pushing the floating paper here and there with the tongs, but her heart was in orbit.

The image of Nora darkened and cleared, and the two women bent over her.

"It's magic," her mother said.

Mackey was crying. Her mother wiped the tears with her sleeve. "Poor, poor baby," she said. Nora regarded them from behind closed lids.

Her mother tapped the table with her fingertips and looked around as if seeing the place for the first time, her voice echoing the rhythm of her hands. "Here we are. Here we are. Here we are."

Allegiance

Some people think travel is unsafe. They don't trust the aeronautic logic of planes, and they think the rest of the earth is more bloody and troubled and roiling than wherever they're from. I'd never been one of those people, though I taught a course called Patterns of Civic Unrest in the Post-Colonial World and I knew more about trouble than most people.

No, my not traveling was because I fell in love with Annabel at eighteen and got married young and had kids early on. A lot of kids, as it turned out. I liked my home life, but I was sorry I never got to go anywhere. I'd always felt odd teaching courses about the global whatever when I'd never been overseas. Once, after Alex, our third, was out of diapers, we were going to leave them all with my parents and go off to Rome for a week. Then Annabel found out she was pregnant with Aaron, which put the kibosh on extra spending.

I suppose I always thought I would have a family, though not so fast. I had steady girlfriends from the time I was fourteen, I hung out in their TV rooms and ate dinners with their siblings. My mother was sure for a while that I was going to marry Viana, the girl I took to my senior prom. Her parents were FOBs, fresh off the boat—they had come from Sicily a generation after everybody else in the neighborhood—and the meals at their house were enough to bring a boy to his knees. Viana herself was fresh and round and smart, but she went off with Eddie DiFranco that summer. She had never been smitten with me, I knew that.

But Annabel was, right away. We met in an economics seminar my first year at Cornell. She was a nervous but eager girl, quite confident underneath that surface fluster. Much of Annabel's power was hidden; she was a tiny redhead, small-boned and lightly freckled, who trained for triathlons. At the end of our first date we had a long, sexy kiss—hungry and inspired—and I thought how particles of lust had been flickering all evening through our fog of conversation. I was ready to go home with these thoughts, as we untangled ourselves, but Annabel, holding my hand, assumed it was time to sneak me into the dorm. I followed in manly silence. She told her half-awake roommate to go sleep on someone's floor across the hall, and then we lay down together, in our lordly freedom. My life was turning out even better than I'd expected.

It might have been my idea, in the early days, that we should pass every day in each other's company, every possible hour. It seemed such a gift to have a craving you didn't have to struggle against. By November, Annabel's roommate requested a transfer, and I became known as Mike the boy who was secretly living in the girls' dorm. When I went home for Christmas, it felt odd to be in my family's old narrow house in Hoboken, a son instead of a lover. I shared a bedroom with my younger brother, Pete, and I still had too much time alone.

Annabel's mother thought she needed to date more people, but blending and binding together so young had advantages. We had some of the dopey intimacy of children—the playful, messy physicality, the shared private customs, the histrionic displays of injury. We settled right in. The fights we had were mostly about money—she came from more of it than I did (though not as much as I pretended); I saw her bossiness as spoiled while she viewed me as arrogantly mingy. I would call her a slumming fake-leftie aristocrat, and she'd call me a macho poor-mouth show-off. Politically, we were both complicated forms of socialists.

We married at the end of junior year. Back in my old neighborhood, Brad Battaglia asked me, "How do you deal with the fidelity thing? You sure you've seen enough of the world?" Richie Cohen said, "When you get as much at home as he does, you don't need extra helpings." I smiled serenely, the well-fed man. I had a wife—what did I need to talk to these guys for?

When Nicholas was born in my first year of graduate school, my secret fear was that I would lose Annabel to him. The fatigues and fascinations of motherhood swept her along, and she hardly knew I was there. My strategy was to kidnap the baby ("the men will go play in the park") and let Annabel swim or run or bike. I knew that even sleep-deprived she hated to stay still. On my lucky days Nicholas came back zonked and ready to nap and Annabel returned buzzing with endorphins and remembering what sex was.

We were living in Ann Arbor then, where I was trying to write my thesis on shifting constructions of marginality in post-war Palermo and whether Sicilians ever believed they were Italians. I was fired up about it, and would work through the night, the obsessed scribbler. When the baby's crying brought me back to where I was, I'd feed him his breast-pumped milk and try to let Annabel sleep.

Annabel always had deep reserves of energy. After Matthew, our second, was born, she started competing in races again. I'd see her on her bike in that weird swimsuit that zipped to the neck, and I'd think how you had to be someone who preferred ecstasy to pleasure to do that. "Honey," she'd say, "you get used to it from practicing." She was very good at focusing, which also made her an ace at statistics, the field in which she was slowly getting her doctorate. And it was her idea to have a third kid. By then we were settled in Bloomington, where I'd gotten a very decent teaching job. She liked having a *group* of kids, she said, a full house, and the town was thronged with nice students who would look after them for cheap.

The fourth baby was a big surprise, and when I went home to the old neighborhood, I faced the usual jibes about not being able to keep it in my pants. Four was a lot, but by then half the people I grew up with had done something weird. Joel Fantoro was in jail in Sri Lanka for smuggling drugs, Angie Lindblad had killed herself in a car in her garage, and Viana LoBianco had run off with a Muslim from some country and her parents had cut her off.

I had to quiz my mother for more of the Viana story. Viana had always been very tight with her family and got angry with me the one time I made fun of their being gushingly protective and old-worldish. I thought she must have fallen in love very hard. She was a sweet girl with a tender nature, and it did not surprise me that she had given herself over to a great attachment. My mother said he was a doctor from Thailand, a very nice boy, who'd come here on a fellowship and had treated Viana for an interesting knee problem. Her parents didn't worry when she was dating him, since he was leaving soon. But then the two began writing back and forth, all the time. It was Viana's father who insisted she break it off. Viana cried, and then she did what he said. But she stopped eating, she hardly spoke, she never slept. "A zombie," my mother said. "She didn't even look pretty anymore." When she began writing to the man again, she didn't lie about it. Her parents told her she had to choose. For months she agonized, and then she grew bitter against her family, and she left.

"Poor Viana," I said. My own parents had been only moderately miffed when I married a non-Catholic. My mother was wholly on Viana's side in this saga. "They lost her, anyway," she said. "So what did they have to break her heart for? I got news for them. It's a bigger world nowadays."

Since I spent my working days talking about what kind of world it was nowadays, I went home and looked up Muslims in Thailand. Plenty of them in the south. There had been local outbreaks in the sixties and seventies—protests against poverty, under-representation, cultural assimilation, the usual—but things had mostly simmered down; in one province, a die-hard band of separatists was still active. With this scanty information, I worked in a reference to it in my next seminar on minority movements, and I probably blushed when I heard myself speaking all of a sudden about Thailand.

I would have liked to write a book about the great mystery of what allows a heavily outnumbered population to ever stop hating the dominant group. And if the fighting ends, how do old enemies manage to live together? There were people you could still talk to, for instance, about the Italian Resistance and how the Partisans went back to towns full of old Fascists trying to be invisible. How did they all walk across the same piazza? But I would have had to travel to ask those questions, and I couldn't see myself making any trips soon. How could Annabel manage four kids by herself? But later I was sorry I hadn't gone.

This was the hardest time for us, with a houseful of banshees under eleven. Once the first two moved into early teenagehood, we didn't have to run around in circles every second, and we could lean on Nicholas or Matthew as babysitters. The summer Aaron turned four, two of them were away at camp and one was working, and the house had a staggering quiet. I noticed I didn't like the way the future felt.

On her side, Annabel was seizing the time to train harder—rising early, working late, whittling her pale body to sinew. It was beyond me why she did this, a type of music I couldn't hear. I was afraid one afternoon when she sat me down for a discussion in the backyard that she was going to start talking again about building a pool we couldn't afford. But she wanted to talk about Steve, her coach. She was having an affair with Steve. Well, she had been having it for seven years. "You must have known," she said. She gave me a tight smile with a lifted brow. "You thought I fucking *knew*," I said, "and closed my fucking eyes?" My house was built on sand, on dry granules of nothing, and was about to be blown away. She wanted a divorce.

All I could voice at first was righteous outrage. More than grief, more than anguish. I couldn't believe she thought she could get away with this. I shouted and roared, and then I was steely and appalled and disgusted. This kind of rank, flagrant injustice couldn't be railroaded through. Not on my watch. It was the sort of unspeakable maneuver that had to be stopped. Right now. "Don't pretend you didn't *know*," she said. And we went on like this for weeks, we couldn't shut up or keep the kids from hearing, and it only got worse. Annabel had been suffering with me for years. This hideous fact (I had to believe her) burned a hole in my heart, a crater. In the end I agreed to move out, because it seemed the least humiliating alternative. I had the kids on weekends.

The first year was very bad. Each of the kids freaked out in his own way—the older boys were sullen, the third was a brat, the littlest was screamingly needy. They came to visit a father who looked like a miserable, red-eyed creature from the deep and who lived in a large hovel of an apartment. Self-pity reeked from the malodorous kitchen.

At meals, one boy would suddenly wax sentimental about the buckwheat pancakes I used to make, how great they were, and another would talk too much about what Steve told them about the White Sox, Steve knew a *lot*. They were like citizens of a country whose borders had changed, confused about where their loyalties fell or on what side their advantages lay. In between their visits I was alone in a way I had never been before.

* * *

In the summer I had them for a month—Annabel was a bit too glad to be free of them—and I took them to see my parents. "August in Hoboken," Nicholas said, "where the elite meet." Aaron, usually the biggest problem, developed a blissful crush on a beautiful five-year-old he met in day camp. Rosa this, Rosa that. She wore fetching red overalls and pink sneakers, and it so happened, according to my brother, Pete, that her mother was Viana.

Viana? How could that be? "She's back living at home," my mother said. "A sad story." Her marriage had busted up? After all that sacrifice? "No," my mother said. "Will you listen?" Viana had been very happy with her husband. "I told you he was a nice fellow," my mother said. They lived in Bangkok, which she loved—who could like that hot weather?—where he doctored poor people. She helped in his clinic. She learned the language, which was not an easy language, but she was a bright girl, wasn't she? She even cooked the food whatever way they eat there. She had a lovely, healthy baby who grew into a cute, cute girl. Her parents never wrote her when she sent pictures. One night Viana and her husband and Rosa were in a car driving back from the countryside when a drunk driver came out of nowhere and ran right into them on the highway. The husband was killed at once, Viana blacked out, the little girl wasn't hurt. While Viana was in the hospital, her parents came and took care of Rosa. Then they all went back to the U.S. together. "End of story," my mother said.

It was only a few days later that I saw Viana herself, at a show put on by the campers. She had always been a soft, bosomy girl and she had thickened some, but what struck me was the freshness still in her face. When I saw her in the audience, she was laughing at a child in a caterpillar costume—a pure, wide-mouthed laugh. I found her afterward, and we hugged as if it were a great joke to see each other. "You're the parent of the astounding Aaron superboy," she said. Aaron was busy ripping off his bee antennae.

Two of my other kids were around me, and I introduced them. When Viana spoke, I could see the sorrow lodged around her chin, the downward tilt of defeat. I suggested a play date between Aaron and the adorable Rosa. Rosa crowed and squealed something like *Dee mahk!* in what I assumed was Thai, and she jumped for joy. "Okay, okay," Viana said, and there were more words between them in that secret language from her other life. She had only been a widow for a few months. I wasn't the sort of asshole to come on to her right then, but I thought she could get used to me again.

So I had a nice August. Viana and I took the kids to the park and hung around our parents' tiny urban yards. We discussed my teaching and the book that I might, who knew, someday write. Viana thought she might go to a school nearby to study nursing. "So you'll stay here?" I said. "Where else do I have to go?" she said. I hated the irony of her being stuck with her family again. "You could go anywhere," I said. "Not me," she said. "Not anymore."

One night I thought she needed cheering up, and I took her— don't ask me why I did this—to a Thai restaurant in the yuppiefied part of town. The waiters, once they heard her speak Thai, could hardly keep from hovering around our table to beam and banter, and they brought us amazing food (though not, Viana said, as good as in Thailand). One of the waiters wore a little white embroidered Muslim prayer cap and was from Pattani, near where her husband's family lived, a disclosure that made both of them cry out in gleeful amazement. Over the dessert of mango and coconut sticky rice, Viana said, "Oh, well. I shouldn't complain, should I? At least I was happy once." What was so awful to me in this sudden bit of bathos was that it showed her trying with all the resolve in her character to have a good attitude.

We had to ask our parents to be sitters when we went out, and this caused massive interest on both sides. I was just what her parents had in mind in the first place, and my mother had always liked Viana. I didn't want anyone badgering Viana—hadn't she been pressured enough in her life? And I didn't want to be talked up as the sensible choice. Never a sexy job.

And once I got back to Bloomington, I did no more than send her chatty e-mail messages. *Aaron has learned to stand on his head. If he can get Alex to hold his feet. Love, Mike.*

Am getting through the days okay, Viana answered. *Rosa misses the ferry we took every day on the Chao Phraya and wants to know when we're going back.* I could see I would have to be patient. All fall I wrote my breezy notes, and for Christmas (which we spent in Indiana) I sent Rosa a ballerina outfit and Viana an expensive book on Italian painting through the ages. She sent me a plaid wool muffler, not exciting, but I wore it for months with a nice, itchy feeling of hope.

I was, of course, haunted by hope. I went to bed with hope every night, with its ghostly brightness settled against my delighted self, and I waited every minute for it to turn and show its teeth. Some men are fools many times over, and maybe I was one of them. I was almost sorry I was bothering with any of this.

The next August, when I came back with the boys, my mother invited Viana and Rosa for the first dinner home. Viana acted slightly embarrassed to see me, and I wondered if she had someone else. It was not until the last week of that humid and highly fraught August that I got a certain vibe while we were shopping for picnic supplies, and I snuck us down to her family's furnished basement while the kids were at my parents'. She giggled as I led her to an ancient leatherette sofa, and with the most straightforward of moves, we became lovers. I got us across that line.

We had slept together when we were teenagers, and though time had gouged and battered and scourged us since, all the nakedness of sex was much easier than it would have been with anyone newly met. Later I wondered if she was very different from when she was seventeen, but I found I could not exactly remember the details from then. Several times I noticed extra things she'd learned, later-formed preferences. But mostly I did not have to think.

It was not really possible to hide our changed status from our families. "Better than that last one," my mother said. "I never liked her being Jewish." Annabel was the most secular of Jews, a post-Marxist atheist who'd hardly been inside a synagogue. "What kind of rotten thing is that to say?" I said. "Viana's a Muslim, if you want to get that way about it." Viana had converted (a simple process, she claimed) to please her husband's parents and have the ceremony they wanted. "*He* didn't care," she said. "He was very modern, very spiritual in a general way. You know what I mean."

My mother decided the conversion didn't count here, much as Viana's parents apparently gave me a familial dispensation for my divorce. I had to be careful around Viana—in the last days of the summer and in our phone calls after—not to rush her but not to seem less than eager. I was truly eager. My mind was flooded with pictures of Viana. Viana was the view out my window, Viana was the water I drank. I had not thought I would fall into such a haze of pure hunger. I didn't want to be desperate or grabby or too cloyingly grateful, though I was all those things. A corner of me could not imagine starting again, and the rest of me did nothing but imagine it every second.

I became a commuter dater; every month I'd fly out. Since Viana was still living with her family, they were unusual dates for adults, blandly chaste or hotly furtive. Sometimes my parents tried to give us some space—this was a bit hilarious to us. "Let them pick a really *long* movie," Viana said, "and stay to watch it twice." Part of her was happy, I did feel that. I could bring her along slowly, if only the others didn't press her. But they did press. Once she phoned me at my school office in tears because her father had told her a husbandless mother was being unfair to her child; her indignation at her father led her to split up with me for a week. I hated her father then, bullying her in his growled Sicilian, evoking a hinterland of fifty years ago, the village he'd gotten the hell out of, as if it were some scriptural landscape.

Not until late spring did I suggest that Viana come to Bloomington for a visit. And then her fleshly presence in the town where I lived, where I'd undergone my whole fucked-up adult history, was almost more than I could bear, and I was a rattled host, hoarse and nervous and all over her. The one thing I could not have expected was that Viana was moved by this. The sight of me unmoored pled my case. She wanted to help, how could she not help? By the end of the weekend, we were engaged.

We were married in June, in Viana's parents' yard. That first summer felt like endless bounty to me; I lived with a woman who laughed with pleasure when she brought me anything I liked—a tiny pale green frog from under the shrubs, an early cup of coffee, a spontaneous bit of lavish invention in bed. She cooked meals so stunning that even Matthew, a real pain about food, decided he liked fish. I thought of this time as Paradise Regained. When I said this, she brought me dates—one of the named fruits in the Garden of Heaven, she said, in the Islamic afterlife—and fed me a few from her fingers. It was an odd feeling to eat them, to chew the dark, sugary fibers and wonder about her old life, what she ate, what she did, though I did not want to be sour or jealous.

She and Rosa still nattered in Thai, though Viana said Rosa was starting to forget words. Once Rosa said, "Hold me upside down, I want to swing over the floor," and Viana said, "Nathavut used to do that." Nathavut was her husband—her first husband. Viana could not say *Nathavut*—on the rare occasions she did—without softening her voice. Rosa had grown in weight since he'd lifted her up to hang like a bat, but I did my best.

When the summer ended, I went back to teaching, and Viana leafed through nursing school catalogues, still dawdling over what to do. I was in my office, eating a terrible Midwestern bagel, when a student ran in with the nutso, hyped-up story that planes had hit the World Trade Center towers on purpose. I was arguing him down when the department secretary came in, and we all spent the next hour looking at the TV set in the lounge. I couldn't believe my eyes, and I'd always thought they were eyes trained to read the world. Some of the students were crying, which made me worry about my own kids, and I called their schools (Annabel was irritated about this later). I remembered I had a wife at home—shouldn't we be comforting each other?—and I drove back. When I came in, Viana was on the telephone speaking Thai. For a second I was sure that her husband was not really dead at all, on this day of the dead, and she was talking to him. She had her hand on her heart when she said goodbye.

It was her brother-in-law, who had just called the house in Hoboken to make sure she was all right. "Oh," she said, when she got off the phone and threw her arms around me, "it's just so hard, it's too much. I hadn't spoken to Winai since I lived there."

Afterwards, this was what I always remembered about that day, though I didn't tell it when all the people I knew were telling their where-I-was stories. After that morning, Viana began sending e-mail to her ex-brother-in-law, who could read English just fine—and through him to the rest of her "old" family, as she called them, especially his mother, who spoke only Yawi, a kind of Malay written in Arabic, and a little Thai. *I am thinking of you in these terrible times*, Viana wrote, at her laptop in the kitchen. An entirely harmless sentiment, and I didn't try to read her incoming e-mail, either. Though I thought of trying.

Meanwhile, my mother told me over the phone that I should make sure I didn't tell anyone Viana was some kind of Muslim because she wasn't, really. "We're both wearing giant neon crosses around our necks," I said. "But my kids have to wear half crosses, half Stars of David."

"You can joke," my mother said. "But people are afraid for a reason."

People were always afraid for a reason—that was what I taught my classes about.

"I couldn't believe it when Nathavut's brother called," Viana said, more often than I liked. "Winai was always kind of stiff-necked, a little full of himself." Now he was the proud recipient of digital photos of Rosa in tap shoes.

How could I resent someone like Viana writing to her ex-in-laws? The news was full of features about how 9/11 made everyone value old bonds of affection. An attachment is not the same as an allegiance. She could be mine and write a few notes overseas. I had a sweet wife; I had no reason to be a grouchy, possessive jerk.

For my birthday in November she put rows of candles all along the walkway of our building, she held out a *torta di ricotta* with my initials in strawberries, and in the doorway Rosa did a special dance for me in her pink tutu. I bragged to everyone at school, I was an unstoppable moron of contentment.

A few weeks later, Viana said to me, "I always like this time of year. When I was in Thailand, we used to go visit the relatives then, when the rains were over. After Ramadan, too, there's a big thing of everybody visiting."

I said I wasn't sure long family visits were my idea of a good time.

"It's very beautiful in Pattani," she said.

"I wouldn't know," I said.

"You'd have to see it," she said. "I can't explain."

"Fine," I said.

But this was a good year for us. Viana knocked herself out for my boys, who were sporadically nice to her. That spring she heard that she'd gotten into nursing school, and the two older boys actually brought home a pizza to congratulate her. Viana herself did a handspring on the lawn. Feet in the air, hair streaming on the grass.

Who knew she could do that? "That's just something I do when I'm happy," she said. I didn't say I'd never seen her do it before.

She was nervous about going back to school, and once it started, she was frantic and frustrated. "*Why* do I want to do this?" she'd say, pushing away some fat expensive textbook. I gave her pep talks about how smart she was, I made my old bachelor Boyardee meals for the kids. She was noticeably less interested in what the rest of us were doing. "Tell me later," she'd say.

Alex said, "You have time for your e-mail."

"She can do what she wants," I said.

"Thank you, thank you," Viana said.

It wasn't until her second year of school that I began to worry. In bed she had become what I would call compliant. She never turned her back, she never refused me, and when I questioned her she always claimed enthusiasm. But I knew. She was a poor liar. The fancier I got, the more determined I was in my attentions, the more unconvincing she was.

I didn't know (how could I?) whether she might have liked any other man better. After Annabel and I broke up, I used to ask myself: what if a person only gets one great love in this life? I didn't really believe that, and people in my place and time generally didn't. But I thought Viana might be the sort of woman who loved only once—his for always, simple as that. A heroine. Whose valor was now being mangled.

The night Pattani was on the TV news, Viana got very upset. "Look what they've done!" she kept saying. "They" were the Thai police, who'd killed a hundred and eight Muslims in the capital of Pattani. Bands of Islamist youth with machetes had attacked police stations and checkpoints, trying to steal firearms. (What a crazy idea, who'd thought that one up, the ungunned trying to rob guns.) Special forces, who'd been tipped off, opened fire, and those left standing took refuge in a sixteenth-century mosque; when the cops couldn't get a surrender, they killed everyone inside. The TV showed a marble floor gouged by grenades and a Koran covered in blood. "This won't help," Viana said. "Do they think this helps anything?"

I thought she sounded like Rodney King asking why we all can't get along. The oldest of all questions. "It's a beautiful mosque," Viana said. "You can't see in the pictures. It was never finished, because of a curse. It's very famous."

"The whole world will be rubble soon," I said.

"You've never seen it. It's a real place. I know it's not real to you."

"It is to you. More than here."

"You have no idea. You've never been anywhere so you can't imagine."

"I can *imagine*," I said. "Do you think all the time of going back? You want to go back."

"People are *dead*. What are you talking about?" she said. "What's the matter with you?"

"I'm not dead," I said, but even I knew I sounded pathetic.

It was a stupid discussion, and what it did (I should have known this, I taught about this) was inspire a deeper loyalty in her to the bloodied mosque, the bullet-pitted brick, the local mourning, her old life. Not a political loyalty, worse than that, a familial one. I probably kept doing it, too, for months and months.

"I know you don't like winter here," I'd say. "You wish Indiana was the tropics, don't you?"

"What if I do?" she'd say. "What, then?"

"Half the time you don't even know you're here."

"What if I don't? Whose business is that?"

Unlike Annabel, Viana was not much of a quarreler, but the rhetorical questions she fended me off with had threats of separation as their answers. A shadow of possibility had entered the house, though we went on as if it had not. A mere shadow can be lived with. That was what I thought.

One Friday Viana was out when I came home, and she wasn't back in time for dinner, though her car was in the driveway. By six all four boys were there, with Rosa, and we waited. I thought maybe her hours had changed at the hospital—a friend might have picked her up—and she'd forgotten to tell me. She was training on the pediatrics ward, which was very high-stress, but how could she forget us? I gave the kids some food, and I called the hospital. The head nurse said crisply that Viana LoBianco was not on duty till Sunday.

My first thought was to hope the head nurse hadn't known I was the husband. In my mortification, I could hardly look at the kids when I hung up the phone. Hadn't I seen the signs? I had, this time. How did it happen that I was a man that two women chose to leave? What had I done? Rosa said, "She better get here soon."

Then I was ashamed of not worrying that something had happened to her, even on the safe streets of Bloomington. She wouldn't just leave Rosa, that was very unlikely. I didn't want to alarm the kids, so I sounded friendly and sheepish when I called the police, who had no news, and then I called patient admissions at Viana's hospital and another nearby. No Viana anywhere, no matter how many times I spelled both her names. By this time Rosa and Aaron were in tears, and Alex was braying at them, "She's okay! She's really okay!" in a loud, scared way. Nicholas had the idea that we should just cruise around, checking the streets and the back roads, and I let the older two go off while I stayed with the others.

I plied them with late-night snacks, but no one was hungry, and Rosa wept into her chocolate milk. *Don't do this to them,* I thought, a prayer in the form of an argument. They were asleep in front of the TV when the older boys came back at two a.m., having found nothing. I was thinking, after I got everyone settled in bed, that if I'd known life was going to be like this, I wouldn't have bothered with any of it.

The phone call came at nine the next morning. All the kids were in the kitchen, and I could hardly hear Viana's breathy voice. She was in a detention facility for women in Indianapolis, where the FBI had taken her, after questioning her for hours about her e-mails to the relatives in Pattani. "What?" I said. "What?" My poor girl, she had to repeat it before I promised to call a lawyer. "Kisses," I said to her, dumbly, as her quarter ran out. I told the kids she would be home soon.

It took three days to get her out, which the lawyer said was much, much better than he had feared. When the lawyer and I went to pick her up, she looked wispy and blowsy and spent, but at home in front of the kids she perked up. "It's over," she sang, and perhaps that was true.

"Your father got me out of there," she told Rosa. When she put her hand on my shoulder, I saw she meant me.

For a week, she had no interest at all in leaving our apartment—she said it looked like the world's coziest nest to her. I wondered that she felt safe there, since it was from this living room that the FBI (a man and a woman) had taken her. She said she just wanted to sleep now. Her questioners had gone at her without letting her sleep very much. They had repeated the same questions in many different ways, and they had done their best to scare her out of her wits. Did she like this jail, would she like to stay here a lot longer? They understood how loyal she might feel to her former relatives, but did she know how serious it was to keep back information? Was it fair to her daughter not to give full answers?

Our lawyer had expressed some surprise that they hadn't questioned me, too, and there was nothing at all to keep them from coming back. I thought about the men's jail, worse than the women's. I kept this fear to myself, since airing it would only have given Viana more dread, to no purpose. I'd spent my whole adult life reading prison memoirs, prison poems, letters from prison—Nelson Mandela, Cesare Pavese, Martin Luther King. I hadn't ever thought that history was going to come find me of all people in this of all ways. The world at my doorstep.

Small noises in the apartment made me jumpy—a phone call at an odd time, a branch hitting the window. But I didn't want to walk around quaking in my own boots; I didn't want to quail before those fuckheads, or act as if I were not equal to what my wife had just gone through, or get Rosa more spooked than she was. I was properly ashamed of being afraid, a useful guide to conduct, since I had my hands full being the steady guy.

In that week that Viana stayed indoors and slept, she liked me to nap with her. Or—she asked—would I just lie next to her until she nodded off? Would I phone her from school later to please wake her up? We held hands over dinner, like a dating couple. She saw me freshly as her rescuer, which was a little ridiculous. Rosa was clingy again, too; she would lay her head on my chest while I was still eating dessert. I liked all this, I liked this time. Perhaps it was not such a bad time for Viana, either.

I did not expect the delicate intensity of these days to last, once Viana went back to nursing school and became again the over-worked woman in white. But something of the generous and melancholic fondness of that time did stay; a shift had been made. For good, it seemed. I could hardly believe this turn of the wheel. It was strange to profit from the scare tactics of a maraud-ing arm of the government, but the irony didn't keep me from being glad.

In public Viana and I were together more, too, talking to jour-nalists, addressing rallies, lined up in a delegation to our con-gressperson, making as much of a fuss as we could. We'd coach each other before and rehash all of it afterwards. Early on, to the kids' great astonishment, we were on a local TV station, for about two seconds. When I saw the tape, I was a little startled at how old we looked. Well, Viana looked better; she was the dark-haired expert on regions whose names she pronounced with rippling exactness, while I, her barking professor of a husband, looked on.

Viana was shy under this glaring attention, but her indignation was deep, and she was too modern, shy or not, to just let me speak. Underneath her wincing she was proud. After someone wrote about us in the *Herald-Times,* I saw her e-mailing the arti-cle to friends in New Jersey.

"So what do they think in Hoboken?" I asked later.

"They think we look like Sonny and Cher," she said. "Just kid-ding. They're pissed off on our behalf, they can't believe it. In Thailand they're always afraid the cops want money, but I told them it's a different problem here."

"You sent the article to Thailand?" I tried not to sound shrill with foreboding. I was worried for Rosa. I was worried for me.

"I did," she said. "I thought about it. I did ask Winai not to tell my mother-in-law—she gets upset, she's been through a lot—but I couldn't really keep it from them. You know?"

I didn't know a thing.

"You don't think I should write to them?"

She already had. How often did she send these notes to them? Every week, every minute? More now than before? She gazed up from her computer, while she waited for me to answer. I waited, too. She had her eyes trained on me, trying to see what I thought, and a terrible expression crossed her face, a look of pained surprise. Was she alone in this after all? Her chin took on its fallen, defeated angle.

"Mike?" she said. I could hardly stand to see her like that.

"Yes," I said. I had principles. A person had a right to send e-mail wherever the hell she wanted. Any jerk could tell her that much, couldn't he? "Of course, you should. Are you kidding?"

Viana looked at me happily, though it was not my happiest moment.

And I thought about those photos of us (Sonny and Cher, indeed) going out into the world as bright pixels emanating from our kitchen table. I'd never exactly understood cyberspace. But here I was, swimming in it—sink or swim—floating on a lake as big as I ever could imagine, bigger. Look what love has done to me, I thought, but it was too small an idea for where I was.

News of the World

We were the News-of-the-World Theater Collective, moving from city to city together; we were all married to each other and to the idea of what you could pull from the streams of the news that ran over and around and through our lives. We wanted no one to ever again let that information splash over them without thinking, so much unnoticed linguistic and conceptual sewage. We were together for six years—in New York, in various U.S. cities during the year when we were touring by bus, and then in San Francisco, where we finally broke apart.

We'd begun working with the news by accident. Our first performance that meant anything to us, before we even had a name, took place in the Brooklyn studio Selene and I shared. With our futon rolled up and chairs set up all around the perimeter of the room, Selene and I mimed lovemaking and fighting, pinning each other's arms and baring our teeth. We dripped red paint on each other and let it run down onto the newspapers we rolled on. I slid across Selene, my breasts against hers, my legs imprisoning her. She shook me off onto my back and let her long, dark hair fall across her face. Even then, she was aware of her beauty as a theatrical element that had to be managed to keep it from being distracting. Boyce—a Midwestern farm boy, a dancer who'd turned to the theater in his thirties—moved towards us, his hands held in menacing positions: starfish, fists, a pantomimed knife thrust. Anson wasn't with us yet.

Meanwhile, at the back of the room, Robert, our director, impresario, and writer, his hands, face, and hair very pale against his black turtleneck, read Milton in an ominous voice: "First, Moloch, horrid king, besmeared with blood / Of human sacrifice and parents' tears..." Our tiny audience was clearly annoyed, but, more than that, *we* could feel it wasn't happening, for them or us.

And then Robert, in a moment of inspired desperation, dropped *Paradise Lost,* picked up a section of smeared newspaper from the floor, and read from it. I wish I could remember the passage. Something violent and ordinary, something you'd never notice if you read it on the train, in the bathroom, over breakfast, on a break. If you felt a little sick afterward, you'd put it down to too much coffee or your breakfast muffin. But when Robert read it, it got through.

In response, Boyce, Selene, and I began to improvise: pulling each other into new shapes, geometric and tense. From that time on, Robert, backstage center, would read lists of the dead from a current war or border conflict, or maybe vivid stories of local crimes and disasters. Anson, upstage, responded with facts and statistics about the oncoming water and food shortages, tsunamis, desertification. Boyce and Selene and I, with our bodies, made news of dance—or vice versa—trying to find new ways of embodying, without miming, the texts. Our strategies to get people to *hear* the news worked for years, and we thought we could do it forever.

Selene's and my final rehearsal—we didn't know it was going to be our last—was for a piece we knew nothing about ahead of time. The company never had much say about which of Robert's ideas we were going to be carrying out, but ordinarily he wasn't mysterious. He was more likely to call us at six a.m. if he had a new idea, to tell us all about it. This time, though, all he said was, "Rehearsals start Tuesday."

On Monday night, Selene and I were in bed playing gin rummy. We played a lot: board games, cards, noisy sexual dramas complete with costumes and role-playing. In our favorite game, we became theatrical impresarios and put on Shakespeare's plays for "acclaim points": *King Lear* was worth more acclaim points than *Cymbeline,* for example. We had five roommates, but also a lock on our bedroom door and thick hangings on every wall.

"Maybe Robert is planning to do something fun," Selene said. "For once. He'd better break it to us slowly or there'll be revolution." We were both naked, propped against the pillows, our cards in our laps, our legs resting against each other.

I said, "Maybe he'll read the spring fashion news and you can strut your stuff for us. It'll be all about the power of beauty and how you make them suffer with longing."

"I'm getting a little old for that stuff," she said. "You idealize me, Joss."

"No, I'm past that stage."

"You *do*," she said, pulling her leg away from mine. "You keep saying to me I'm the most beautiful woman in the world, and it's nice, but it's also pressure. I was pretty in my twenties. Now I'm interested in other things."

"You'll always be beautiful," I said. "Even when you're a white-haired old thing, strangers will still stop in the street to stare at you." Her fall of hair, the way her cheek curved down to her lips, her body—all of this would have made her a star in any seraglio. As for me, I looked like a scrawny, smartass boy. I was a painter before I was a dancer before I was an actress: most often, I played the part of the astonished victim, the one the audience is supposed to identify with.

She dropped all the cards on the floor, and then lay on her side, her back to me. I looked down at her from above, seeing how the bedside lamp—a handmade affair of old seashells we found at a thrift shop—illuminated her eyelashes against her perfect cheeks. I was a little miffed, but decided to let it go. It made me puff up with pride that this stunning creature belonged to me, that I was the one who gave her pleasure, looked after her. But it wasn't such a bad deal for her, either. She required a lot of looking after, my Selene, like a large and sometimes bad-tempered Persian cat, needing constant attention, unable to tolerate unpleasant food or too much sunlight or wind, easily lost in strange cities. I put my arm around her, and she snuggled up to me, the length of her body against mine.

When we arrived in the Mission the next day, the usual guys stood on the corner in front of the Dollar Store next to the building that held our rehearsal space. Unshaven, staggering, given to fights. They tended to wear old army fatigues or jeans, their caps pulled over their eyes. One of them said to her, "Honey, can I have a light?" An old guy, the smell of fear, anger, and alcohol drifting off him.

She turned towards him, her face opening up. She doesn't smoke and certainly didn't have a light, but she was going to find some way to help him, talk with him, and maybe listen to his problems for the next hour. I began steering her toward the gate over the gallery door. "Not tonight," I said to him.

"I wasn't talking to you, baby dyke," he said, looking startled, as if he hadn't realized I was there until I spoke. I smiled at him, and shepherded her inside.

The performance space we usually used was above a nonprofit gallery, with space for thirty chairs, which we set up ourselves on show nights. The gallery displayed work by new young artists— work that sometimes set our minds on fire and sometimes embarrassed us—vials of bull's blood and photos of blurred fields or pointillist cityscapes. Though the room upstairs was a blank box, the gallery itself had a huge wall of windows, the light slightly dimmed by an iron gating looking out onto the dirt and primary colors of Mission Street. I always felt a little suffocated, leaving it all behind to go up into the white, windowless, enclosed room.

When we saw the huge photos Robert had pinned on the walls of the performance space, Selene wheeled around, staring. She'd refused to look at the pictures when they first came out. Now she gagged once, then swallowed. I put my arm around her.

I'd seen the images when the rest of the world had seen them, but not like this. Robert had spent something, getting color photos blown up so that the humans in them were larger than life-size, the camouflage of the fatigues showing brown and green, the blood bright against skin and floor. Naked bodies, smeared with mud or shit, some clutching each other, lying in piles. One man crouching in fear of a black dog, a hall of shiny metal doors behind him, his hands up almost across his face. Bags over the heads. Raw wounds, bandaged or not. Soldiers with guns and smiles, a girl with a leash. Another girl in fatigues crouching beside an anonymous body, half covered here and there by bloody cloth. The scissors she held next to the fresh raw wounds. A man in fatigues beside her, both of them in dark watch caps. Her face, her tilted head, her smile, the gloved hand giving a thumbs-up. And then there she was again, over the body of an unshaven, bandaged man, his dead eyes closed, ice packed up to his neck. Her smile—what was that smile? She was the one I couldn't look at. It was like suddenly coming up against a funhouse mirror.

Robert leaned against a wall, dramatically enacting both the seriousness of his determination to carry out this new idea and his attentive interest in our responses. He was very tall, with white blond hair and skin; his face looked as if it had been smashed with a hammer and put back together a little too quickly. Anson and Boyce sat on the floor, glum, their bodies and faces saying they wished we weren't about to do this project. One or another of us sometimes said to Robert, "We're a collective; maybe we should make decisions together about what we're going to do next." To which Robert would say, "Dears, as far as I'm concerned, every one of you could run the Royal Shakespeare Company. But, as it's worked out, I happen to be the director of *this* company. So could you just trust me?" He'd gone to Julliard, unlike the rest of us, and was a wizard with funders.

Boyce said, "I thought we did *current* news. Why not do the Crimean War? How about My Lai?" He went on, "I'm not sure what we're going to add to these. We could just stand naked in front of them and do nothing." We had a kind of friendly, brotherly rivalry—he was a better dancer than I was and often seemed to be making some move to show off. His tacit job in the company was to say to Robert what no one else could.

"I don't know who would come to the performances, or why," Anson said. Boyce's best friend and physical opposite—dark, slim, always in leather and chains, given to sudden delighted smiles, particularly good with children. He sang or did beatbox and toning, his readings incantatory. Any newspaper or advertising fragment sounded like a call to another world, coming from Anson. It was *not* his job to stand up to Robert, which he knew very well. Suddenly there'd be no money for his position for a month, or Robert would be unable to support him in getting a particular teaching job, or not a single one of his ideas would make it into the new performance. But Anson persisted: "Maybe creeps getting off on the pictures."

"Or people who enjoy feeling indignant and then heading home to the suburbs," Boyce said, frowning at Anson—a look meaning, "Back off and let me handle this."

Selene, either because she was genuinely upset or to distract Robert, gave a huge sigh and reached out to him. He put his arms around her, and she rested her head on his shoulder. Back when I was a painter, I had sex with men sometimes. I still occasionally feel the attraction, though not as much. None of the people I used to sleep with seem quite real now, though I wanted them badly at the time. I'd been faithful to Selene, but I didn't know about her.

She'd said to me, a couple of months earlier, after a particularly exhilarating rehearsal, "If you and I were to have a baby, maybe Robert could be the father." I was afraid to ask if she'd ever slept with him or if she was thinking about it: he certainly acted in public as if she belonged to him.

I said to her, often, that we could leave and go elsewhere. Back to New York—we'd loved Brooklyn. Or Chicago. Someplace where we weren't always negotiating how to maneuver around Robert.

"What other company would take us both on? And could you go back to just dancing after this?" she said. Robert was great at money—he got grant after grant, and none of us had to work more than part-time at day jobs during show times. And to what extent were all of our best ideas a result of Robert's suggestions and prodding?

Robert, gently wiping the sweat from Selene's face with a hand-kerchief, said, "My baby."

Before I could stop myself, I said, "*My* baby, technically speaking."

He looked over at me and said, "Joss"—a comical reproach, so full of warmth and complicit amusement that I found myself returning his smile. Then he turned to the group. "I have readings for you all. Selene, you can start with the trial transcripts." He handed out a stack of articles, and we sat down with them. After twenty minutes, Selene said, "Are you going to read these during the performance?"

"I want to watch you work first," he said, his tone inviting us into a marvelous and serious game. "Then I'll know if we read from these or find something else."

For the next hour and a half, we traded articles, lying on the blue exercise mats, moving to uncomfortable folding chairs, standing for a while, leaning against the walls, careful not to touch the photos. We had food, but no one was eating.

The descriptions of the special access program—an entire secret military life with no checks or accountability... "the black guys," with all their hidden power and unlimited approval to capture, interrogate, and kill "high-value targets." And then "the white guys" moving about in the sunlight, making speeches and denying all knowledge.

The detainees were moved from prison to prison so that even the system itself often lost track of where they were. Almost every source pointed out that information extracted by torture was likely to be useless invention. Most of these pieces said very little about the stuff that had been all over the TVs and daily news—the ongoing sexual party, the lurid details of who was sleeping together, who had gotten who pregnant. The guards had been told to "soften up the detainees," but who were the others in these pictures, in the testimony? What might those insane, cheerful, proud smiles be expressing?

I caught myself trying to imagine how to dance this, and then was afraid I'd humiliate myself by throwing up in the rehearsal hall. Another part of my brain observed that this would be a genuine, human response. Or else it would be the result of an unconscious desire to have a human response. I said, "There is nothing we can do to add to, explain, or ameliorate any of this. Actually, it would be disgusting. We're not going to change anything by doing a dance; we'd be like a lot of head lice. And Boyce is right—this isn't news. It's too far in the past."

Robert stood, grandly, before the photographs. "The country saw these and took them for granted." During his explanations and exhortations, the magic usually kicked in—the sense he could create, as no one else, of including each of us in a charmed inner circle. "A few people were punished, we all felt better, and the mechanisms that foster torture continue untouched. We need to find a way to make people *pay attention.*"

"Ten or eleven at a time," I said, putting down my article. "Unless we get a full house. I don't think we should do this."

"I knew when I came in today," said Robert, "that I'd be attacked. Often those with the least confidence in their own ability to take on artistic challenges are the most vocal in resisting them."

"I didn't say I'm not up to it. I said it would be pointless."

Selene poked me in the side, and Anson said, quickly, "I suppose the way in which we tackle it would depend on the results we were after. Who do we imagine as our audience for this piece? Those who haven't yet been able to take in the information, or people for whom we could illuminate it in some way?"

"The strays and the converted," Boyce said.

Selene said, "I wish we could do stories about heroism. Maybe, if we gave people a positive example, they'd walk out of the theater and quit their ugly jobs. Go to meetings, vote, march, get others to vote, raise money, and write letters. Die for their beliefs."

"You have an original mind," Robert said. "That's your charm. You are a lovely creature with no clue about anything, and somehow that becomes your great strength."

She turned to look at him, her face taking on an expression of betrayed fury. She opened her mouth, but then Boyce leaned forward. "Hey, did you realize that Joss looks like her?" he said, pointing at the central photograph, the body in ice with its bandaged face, the grinning girl above. Robert was smiling, his eyebrow up again, as if this were part of his plan. Maybe he was just quick to catch a cue. Selene sat back, breathing deeply. She looked down at the pale, polished wood of the floor and began to make patterns in the dust with one finger.

Robert said to Boyce, "Lie on the ground with your arms behind your back." He turned to me. "Kneel beside him. Menace him in some way."

"Absolutely not." I picked up my jacket and headed for the door. "Come on, Selene."

"Joss," said Selene. Any evidence of anger had disappeared; we'd find out later if it had gone underground, if she got a migraine. She'd been having a series of them after a demonstration where we'd gotten stuck in the hot sun. I'd told her, before we ever went out, that she'd be better off staying home, but she'd never known her own limits.

Boyce said, "Let's just try it out. Maybe we really can touch people in some way, maybe this will make them take some action, like Selene said."

"What action would that be?" I said, but I put down my jacket. Boyce lay down, pulling his sweater over his head as if it were a hood, holding his wrists together. I knelt over him and pushed him in the shoulder, hard enough to roll him to the side. Then I pulled back, feeling a little sick.

"That's good," said Robert. He looked at Selene, who dropped to the other side, lying next to Boyce, her own arms behind her back. Robert then looked at Anson, who picked up the articles and flipped through them. In a newscaster's voice, he said, "The President 'is sorry that people seeing these pictures didn't understand the true nature and heart of America.'" He frowned and tried again. "The Secretary of Defense has described the detainees as 'unlawful combatants.' As such, he says, they 'do not have any rights under the Geneva Convention.'" He said, "It sounds like I'm being ironic." He tried an ordinary voice: "Seymour Hersh says, '...of course, Saddam tortured and killed his people. And now we're doing it.'"

Boyce curled into a ball and began to inch away, leaving me kneeling over Selene, who pressed her wrists together and arched her back. I leaned across her, placing a spread-out hand over Boyce's face, against the wool of his sweater. Selene and I caught each other's eyes, then dropped our poses and turned away. Anson looked up from the pages and said, "It's not believable." He shook his head, helplessly.

Boyce said, "All we're doing is reenacting it. Why don't you stand there and read the accounts of Milgram and those experimental subjects who went on turning up the shocks? Joss could work the controls."

Robert said, "Joss, you're a guard. Tie up Selene."

I unbuckled my belt, slid it out of my jeans, and wrapped it around her wrists, pulling the leather through the buckle. She jerked in surprise, though I was trying to be gentle. We'd played some bed games with velvet handcuffs and blindfolds; now it was as if a nightmarish version of our private life were happening in public. Trying to act as if this meant nothing to me, I said to Robert, "The prisoners should be wearing fewer clothes."

"Why don't you take off *your* clothes?" said Boyce, muffled by his sweater.

"I don't believe you as a guard," said Robert. "You're a Girl Scout, learning to do rope tricks. Stop trying to make us like you. Think of the worst thing you've ever done."

Looking around the room, I could see that everyone had been sent back to—what kind of memories? Boyce had broken his father's nose once, but that was retaliation, when he finally got big enough to protect himself and his sister. Selene hadn't spoken to her parents in five years—she came from a part of the Midwest where they think there's something wrong with people like us. I tried to think of my own worst thing, but everything seemed so low-grade. I'd left one scary, pathetic girlfriend by refusing to return her calls or e-mails. I'd given away a friend's secrets in sixth grade—her bed-wetting and eating spoonfuls of sand—and then pretended not to know who had left her subject to endless tormenting. When my friends were shoplifting in junior high, I made sure to be in another part of the store, in case they were caught. Robert was right: every gesture I made, on or off stage, showed my cowardice and yearning to be approved of. I couldn't be dazzling, but I could be *nice*. Above me, in the central panel, the girl grinned: she had stepped across a divide, and the photo proved it. She was a citizen of a new country now.

I yanked on the belt, tightening it around Selene's hands. Her back arched, inadvertently this time, and she rolled over, the belt beneath her, her shirt twisting up to reveal the skin underneath. After a moment, I raised my thumb, smiling up at Robert.

There was a long silence, the rest of them staring at me. Selene shook herself free and backed away. Anson put his arm around her. Robert didn't seem to know what to do next. "Not the thumb," he said, finally.

"The thumb is really...she should do it," said Anson. He spoke with some urgency, and I could see the others nodding, even Selene. No one was looking at Robert. They were watching me alertly, waiting to see what I'd invent next.

"I think we have to have the thumb," I said.

Robert frowned and stood up very straight, making himself taller. "Don't start enjoying this," he said. "That would be taking it a little far."

"I'm not enjoying anything," I said. My head was floating.

"You're not such a good girl after all, are you, Joss? You see you can cause pain and like it." And then he changed his tone, squatting beside me and putting his hand on my arm in what appeared to be a kindly gesture. He murmured, comforting me, "I know how hard it can be to mix your work and personal life and what it must be like to be in your position. I just want you to know that you do have an essential, a *special* role in the company. We have to have a Selene, but think how impossible it would be to put on any show without people like you as well."

As if some central channel had opened inside me, a wild red

rage blew up and through the top—out my head, out my mouth. It felt wonderful. "Take your fucking hands off me," I said, my voice shaking, hissing into his face, feeling myself become monstrous, my face a distorted mask. "I feel *violated* when you touch me. You don't know a goddamn thing about me or my relationship or anything else at all. Don't call us at six a.m. anymore. Don't touch either of us. Don't pretend you care about me in any way, shape, or form, or that you want me in this company for any reason besides that I'm here to look after Selene. At least I'm not a person who *lives* to be admired and then behaves like a total, pathetic, bullying *brigand*." All the air went out of me then—it had seemed I was saying something, but I realized it was all stupid. Brigand, who said brigand anymore? I didn't know if I even believed what I'd said or if I'd tricked myself into letting Robert set the terms of my defiance. He was so much smarter than I was.

Everyone was staring at me as if I were radioactive. Selene was crying. Robert's face had gone very still. "You'll need to come and talk to me in the morning." It was clear from the unmitigated coldness in his voice that he was planning to fire me. "First thing." Then he said to everyone else, in an almost normal voice, "We'll call it quits for the night. Go home, do some freewrites, see what you think. We'll start again in a couple of days and I'll have some choreography for you, based on what I've seen here."

He usually said, "Good work!" no matter how bad we were, and for that moment, however often we heard it, there was a wonderful sense of absolution. I'd left so many rehearsals and performances remembering that, after all, I loved to be in his company, and there was no one else more magical. He began unpinning and rolling the photographs, Boyce on the opposite wall, working their way toward that central panel.

On the way home, Selene said, "Are you crazy." It wasn't a question. I shrugged, and she said, "I can fix this, if you let me." We were on a night bus: drunks and crackheads, kids in their fishnets and piercings on their way to the clubs, teenagers inhabiting their story about their gang life. Selene always sat by the window; I was on the inside, between her and the crazies.

I said, "I do believe I've remembered the worst thing I ever did. All of them. It's things I *didn't* do. People who were hoping I'd look after them. My mother, when she first got her diagnosis. She was living with two cats in a little condo at the end of a long and nauseating bus ride to the hospital; she hinted she'd be better off staying with someone, and I pretended not to understand her."

I'd never told anyone about this before, not even Selene, and I looked out the window, not at her face. My voice was low so no one else on the bus would hear, and I half hoped she wouldn't hear, either. "I was in *Medea* then, a small part, but a big production, my first real chance after college. It seemed that if I let this opportunity go by, I might not have another one. Sometimes a neighbor took Mom for her chemo, and I said to myself the woman was the sort of person who doesn't have enough going on in her life and needs to be helpful, that I was doing quite a bit by going to visit my mother for a couple of hours once a week, calling her every few days on the phone. That we all have different sorts of gifts—I was an artist, not a caretaker. I thought my mother might live a long time, and I couldn't imagine having her with me. In the end, it was only five months. But even those weekly visits made me crazy with nerves."

Selene touched my leg, and I took a quick look at her face, which was trying not to express judgment. Selene, who wouldn't even have left a sick stranger alone, couldn't comprehend what I was saying. She might have been thinking about what it would mean for her in the future.

I said, "Now I send a little money to various organizations and write some letters or e-mails, but what have I ever risked to try to stop things being done, right now, by my own country? I just sit in my house and let the cattle cars go by. I'm a cold person, Selene. There's something damaged inside me." Maybe I was hoping she'd contradict me, tell me how I loved her, and then I'd say she was the only one. But she just took my hand. I went on, "Don't even think about getting in between me and Robert. I'm through with wheedling and giving in and letting you be charming for me."

Selene, looking doubtful, squeezed my hand. She didn't think I could overcome him, but she was wrong. I knew where his soft underbelly lay, and, for the first time, I was willing to put in the knife to get my way. His power lay in his ability to charm and confuse us, never to go after more than one of us at once, to put us in the position where we didn't feel safe defying him. Inside, though, he was as frightened and ashamed as anyone, afraid he'd lose his command over us, afraid we'd stop worshipping him. If I just kept showing up and cheerfully doing my parts, he would have to let it blow over rather than risk a full-out insurrection. He'd be able to see I wasn't afraid of him anymore. If he interfered with me, I might say anything to them about him, and his control over the company would be gone.

That night, Selene was in bed before me. I'd sat down on the couch at nine and then found I was so tired I couldn't get up to wash my face. Our housemates came and went, on their way to bed. Finally I decided to skip the face-washing and turned off the living room light. When I went into the bedroom, a woman lay in my bed, the covers pulled up to her chin. She was on her side facing me. She opened her eyes.

"Hey," I said. "Are you *naked* under the covers?" I'd meant it as a joke, but found that some part of me was shocked at the idea. Who was this woman in my bed? She looked familiar and not-familiar at the same time. It was a little sexy, but more frightening. Was I supposed to climb under the covers and sleep beside her? And I didn't know who I was. I didn't recognize myself.

"Of course I am." She smiled at me in what seemed like obscene invitation.

"I don't think I can get in there if you're naked."

"What are you talking about?" The smile went away. My sense of dislocation was worse. She said, "Joss?"

"I don't think I know you. I can't get in bed with a naked stranger."

She gave me a look that said she was tired of this, then threw back the covers. A well-fed, pampered, muscled adult body—wrinkled nipples, strange patch of pubic hair, soft belly. I let out a scream.

She sat up and grabbed the covers, shielding herself. "What's the matter with you? What are you doing?"

I couldn't say anything, just shook my head. Selene, who never had to ask what I was thinking, began to cry. And that was a little bit of a pleasure, though I wasn't admitting it to myself. She was seeing herself through my eyes, frail and weak—stripped, for once, of her beauty. I didn't say anything, just stood there. Then, feeling ill, I put my hands over my mouth.

I ran into the bathroom, dying to get clean. I was afraid some member of the household would intervene or come in to find out what was happening, but no one did. I put water on my face, then washed my face and neck several times. I brushed my teeth again. When I went back to our room, she was curled up, facing away, the covers over her ears. By now it seemed like an odd joke of some kind—all my feelings for her had returned, and I couldn't entirely remember that other state. I was Joss Brown, who'd been the football mascot in high school and who longed for a day at the beach with no knowledge of anything happening anywhere in the world.

When I got into bed, though, and tried to put my arms around Selene, she jerked away from me. "My feelings are hurt," she said.

"Are you kidding? We were sort of playing, right?" I had myself almost convinced.

"You looked at me and screamed." Her voice was blank, no emoting at all.

I moved closer, nuzzling her hair. "My leopard, my Selene, sweetheart." After a while, she started to relax, though she still held herself away from me.

"We're not going back there," I said. She didn't answer for a while, and I said, "Selene, we're done with those people. With that company."

If I'd thought about it, I would have assumed we'd have an argument that would last for days. I was willing to fight as long and hard as necessary. There was no way I wouldn't win—when it came down to it, she couldn't live without me, either. Instead, there was another period of silence. I couldn't see her face, and couldn't tell whether she was angry, sad, frightened, reflective.

Finally, she said, "Yes, okay. But then I want to have a really different kind of life. I want to be able to move around, to go wherever the good parts are. I don't want us to always have to perform together." I nodded, nuzzling her ear, making a trade that was going to cost plenty, as it would turn out.

We'd forgotten what daily life in the theater was like for most people: waiting tables during the day, taking time off for auditions, getting commercial work sometimes, very occasionally the work we wanted to do, and, more often than we liked, no work at all. It became clear, after a couple of years, that I'd dropped out of one category and into another. When you've been playing regional dinner theater—Ado Annie in *Oklahoma* or a junior hyena in *The Lion King*—it becomes harder and harder to get other kinds of roles, and, in the process, the very nature and intent of your performances begin to change.

Our games, in and out of bed, ground to an end. A couple of times I tried getting out our costumes or the dice that told us which parts of each other's bodies to kiss, but Selene said, "I think we've outgrown all that, don't you?" We fight less, but we're more sharp-tongued about small irritations and no longer tell each other everything. After a while, I became almost certain that she was sleeping with other people. Being with her is still better than being alone, though, and maybe every couple gets to this point sooner or later. My hope is that, sometime in the future, we'll get over it again: there's a kindness I see sometimes in old couples where one or both of them has been close to death.

In the morning, we made love for the first time with the new feeling of separation between us, but when I thought of the night before, it seemed like part of some dream. And anyway it had been a small, irrelevant event. No prisoners held on leashes in a cold prison with the threat of death over them, moved from prison to prison so their families couldn't find them, hooded and standing on boxes, thinking the wires attached to them were live and they'd be electrocuted. No one beaten, no one with lit cigarettes pressed into their ears. And even if someone were to say that I could have done all of these things, under the right circumstances—if I'd been told to "soften them up" by a higher command, if I thought they were my enemies—they'd be wrong. If I'd been in Milgram's lab, I would have refused to deliver the shocks, or at least the highest level of the shocks. But I didn't know who I was during the improv and in that moment when I didn't recognize Selene or myself. And I wasn't willing to take one more step down that road. I didn't know what kinds of things I might be capable of if I lived indefinitely in the country of the strong.

Change of Address

When I was in fifth grade at a private school for boys in Newton, Massachusetts, my geography teacher, Mr. Neale, was blind, had been blind for some years, probably on account of some gradual degenerative disease. This was in 1952. Mr. Neale was a large man, with a round face and thick fleshy ears; his hair was white, and his eyes were hidden behind a perpetual furrow. All the other masters (yes, in the English style, teachers were called "masters") revered Mr. Neale, but he was not popular with the boys. I say that his loss of sight must have been gradual because before his "light was spent" (Mr. Grant, eighth-grade English) he had memorized his textbook, and his method of teaching was this: each day he selected a boy, apparently at random, to come forward and sit beside him at his desk. The text was open in front of him, and he instructed the boy to turn to a certain page, and then, often pointing with his beefy, white-flaked finger, he would ask the boy to read aloud the third paragraph of the first column, or perhaps the caption under the sepia photographs of dhows assail with the pyramids of Giza in the background. A lecture would follow, with questions stabbed out without warning—because there could be no warning—at the boy squirming in the back, or whispering next to the door. Occasionally Mr. Neale's finger, or shirt cuff, or necktie would obscure the selected passage, and the boy would have to say, "Excuse me, Mr. Neale, but I can't read it," and he would answer, with an irony none of us could miss, "I see your problem, boy."

So it went for the year, as it had gone for many years before, and along the way every boy in the class became aware of the fact that we were being shuffled and manipulated through a circumspected space ruled by obscure laws and rigid geometries, which is to say, the space in the eyes of a blind man. Take this matter of the apparently random selection of the day's assistant. No one wanted to do this, each dreaded his name being called out; the worst, of course, was on Fridays, when the boy would have to read out loud, one by one, mistakes writ large, the answers given on the week's quiz, starting with his own. Mr. Neale gave tough quizzes. For these reasons, we all kept a scorecard of how many times we each had been called. Even if it seemed that he had called one of us three times in a row, at the end of the month or of the term, the number of times each one had been selected was equal. I wonder even today how Mr. Neale did this. He must have been following some mathematical progression based on the alphabetical order of our names or our placement in the rows of assigned desks, but the effect on a class of ten-year-old boys was to baffle and subsume us. We recognized that resistance was hopeless, that it was our fate to be drawn into the opaque and immutable, into a sort of parallel world where everything we thought was true was not, but where, if we worked, we might receive the dark gift of wisdom.

Immutable this world, Mr. Neale's world, was in another respect. This text that he had memorized had been published in the late twenties when the ink on the Treaty of Versailles was still damp. This should not have been much of a problem: rivers and mountain ranges and continents don't change much in twenty years, and as for the boundaries and names of countries in Europe and Asia, Mr. Neale might well have instructed us that although Poland, for example, seemed a massive and quite menacing power on the maps we were studying, it was now a much smaller war-ravished nation sliding daily into Stalin's iron palm. But Mr. Neale didn't do this, and he may have been right: in those days we children were hearing plenty about the Soviet Union and relentless encroachment, and we practiced weekly our duck and cover in the assembly room behind black-out curtains that made us feel we were being shut into a mass grave. Mr. Neale offered us a different view of history, a calmer, less eschatological take on the current climate, a certain faith in persistence. So it was that the world we learned about in 1952, the world whose features and wonders we memorized in that airless and timeless classroom, that world whose maps we colored in and capital cities we located and named, whose leaders wore high starched collars and top hats and whose peoples seemed often to wear grass skirts and nose rings, whose principal modes of transportation seemed to be the camel and water buffalo, a world whose future, in a sense, we tried to anticipate and even, through the force of our studies, to influence, in 1952, was the world of 1925.

This may have seemed more of a disconnect to me than it did to my friends and classmates. My mother had died when I was four years old, and I was raised by a young Hungarian woman named Magda Vasary, who had originally come to Cambridge as a refugee during the war and had been employed as one of the counter girls at a humanitarian Cambridge establishment called the Window Shop Bakery. In its last incarnation it was on Brattle Street. The space is now called the Blacksmith House and is best known as a venue for readings by local poets and novelists. All of the women who worked at the Window Shop were DPs, led by two aristocratic Austrians who had landed in the U.S. with little more than their proud names and their grandmothers' recipes, and the cookies and pastries from the Window Shop were legendary. Magda often took me there to visit with her friends, and I was allowed to select a cookie and given a glass of milk and then seated in the kitchen bathed in the yeasty glow of raspberry tarts and cinnamon bread, while the girls chatted away in two or three different languages. They were all beautiful, those European counter girls of the Window Shop, and one by one they were courted and snatched away by other young émigrés, and I was taken to their weddings in Cambridge and Watertown, some of them in Roman Catholic churches, some in synagogues, but all of them conducted in German. What I remember best of them were the dark narrow-faced men in heavy wool suits with fat lapels, the old women in black, and the brides covered in yellowing lace.

My father was an academic, a professor of English, and though we lived in a vast Victorian house in Cambridge and anyone meeting him immediately assumed that he taught at Harvard, the truth was he taught at a small junior college in Boston called Garland, long defunct, not much more than a secretarial school for the less-talented daughters of rich WASPs. He was gangly, a skeletal face improbably dominated by a bulbous nose, an odd-looking man. He had a forelock of spiky hair that always stuck rigidly upwards, no matter what he might do to it. I have the same nose, and the same hair. My father was, as far as I know, the entire English department, maybe the only man on the faculty, and though his students were being trained as typists, teachers of penmanship and home economics, or simply as competent housewives, they nevertheless knew their Milton ("light was spent"). He insisted on being addressed as "Professor." I have no memory as a child of seeing him without a necktie. My much older brother, Teddy, had long ago been shipped away to prep school, and to college, and his vacations home in those early days were magic to me, the reassuring male rumble of his conversations over cocktails with our father, Magda's laughter from the kitchen as he teased her about her accent, her formal European manners. We ate as a family in the dining room when he was home, the four of us, and sometimes Teddy invited me into his room for "bull sessions" surrounded by his athletic trophies and car magazines. But I knew little about his life, what work he did after he finished college and moved to New York. I don't even know now what his career has been, though I could call him up and ask, if the phone number he had in 1959 still works.

In my estimation, Magda was the most beautiful of all the Window Shop girls. She was tall; her skin was perfect; her hair, thick and blond, probably would have been worn long and bound in a bun at home, but in her flight across Europe she had cut it boyishly short. She looked like Audrey Hepburn. She never dressed for beauty, and described herself as plain. She was especially dissatisfied with her hands, which she called "stubby peasant hands." I wasn't fooled. Men stopped and gaped when we walked down the street, which made me proud and smug because only I, I thought, got to see her in the middle of the night coming out of the moon in her nightgown to comfort me after a nightmare. Oh, there is much about my memory of her in those days that is deeply erotic. In the summers she took me swimming at a pool club in Belmont. I can imagine that in those days there may have been a rule that employees of members would not be allowed to swim, but no one ever complained when Magda appeared in her bathing suit.

My father's housekeeper in those days was an Irish woman named Donnie O'Brien, and she was a very nice lady who was kind and loving to me, but even then I could discern that she was ugly, a squat person with bumps on her face and sparse hair. During the time Donnie worked for us she married an older man she always referred to as Mr. George, and for all I know she called

him Mr. George at home. When my father happened to en-
counter him in the morning or evening, he called him George,
but as my father was equally likely to refer to a working-class man
by either his first name or by his last name without a title, his full
name remains a mystery. Mr. George called my father Professor.
Mr. George dropped Donnie off in the morning in his black pre-
war Chevrolet, and often he spent the entire day in his car at the
curb in front of our house, with feathers of cigarette smoke escaping through a slightly opened window. I wonder about this capacity for waiting, waiting in silence hour by hour, with perhaps only
a newspaper to read and reread, so unimaginable today but not at
all unusual then. At the end of the day he usually came in the
kitchen door to pick up Donnie, to help her carry a bundle of
sewing or leftovers that she was taking home, and he was unfailingly solicitous to her; he treated her like a young and precious
bride. He seemed not to like Magda; I didn't know why.

Once Donnie was gone the long evenings began, and they
seemed endless, as if the ticking of the grandfather clock in the
hall of our house slowed down for these hours, as if the loneliness
of my father's nightly martini, taken alone in the living room,
stretched time. After Magda and I had eaten supper she often sent
me in to talk to him, and he always immediately put down his
book when I entered, sat back and crossed his long, slender legs,
and sometimes lit a Chesterfield, which meant I had to remain
there with him until it was fully smoked, the longest-lasting cigarette ever invented. I loved my father; I don't want it to appear
otherwise, but I didn't know him very well. He would ask me
about my day in school, and it always seemed that I should preface
my answer by telling him what grade I was in, what subjects I was
studying, who my friends were. It never occurred to me to ask him
how his day had gone, even after I had reached the age that this
would have been an obvious question and a good way to get me
off the conversational spot. Simply put, I didn't want to go there,
into my father's sorrows, the loss of his wife, into my father's disappointments, the way his career had gone, into his work, those
pages and pages of scribbled manuscripts that never seemed to
leave his study, into his solitudes, which seemed complete.

Magda and I spent our evenings in the kitchen, where she did
chores, wrote her letters home, and where I did my homework

under her supervision and from time to time with her instruction. I picture her wearing a light blue cashmere cardigan that makes her shoulders look small and delicate, and I can picture the letters, with their unfamiliar stamps and foreign penmanship, the ones that bounced their way back and forward across Europe, in and out of the Iron Curtain, across the Atlantic, only in the end to find her, care of my father's name, in Cambridge, Massachusetts. Whenever I hear the scrape of a fountain pen across a sheet of rag bond—it's been a while now, I admit—I think of her in those hours of those days.

Her English, which she had studied with a tutor in Hungary, was good, but sometimes a little garbled, and in syntax especially my grasp of the subject had a bilingual flavor. I developed a strange library of suffixes and never seemed to know where to place my verbs, which the masters at my school seemed to take in stride. As I grew older I was encouraged to study on my own in my room, but I always found an excuse to bring my work back to the kitchen. Magda was good in math, which was luck for me after I began algebra in the seventh grade, since I was and am hopeless in math.

When the work was done we would head upstairs, in my earlier years to my bath and bedtime story—most often, a Hungarian folk tale—and later, to my own private nighttime rituals. Once we had vacated the kitchen my father came in to cook his supper. Cooking, in fact, was his one hobby, the one pastime that seemed fully to engage him. He kept his cookbooks in his study. A couple of times each week he called Sage's Market with his orders of rather exotic ingredients, which were stored separate from the household food selected by Magda and Donnie. I'd hear him down there as I was falling asleep, the frenetic ting of a whisk against the side of a mixing bowl, the screech of the springs on the oven door, an occasional slam of a pot on the grate if something went awry. Magda was usually upstairs by then, in her rooms on the third floor, listening to the radio, humming along to a Bing Crosby tune or an air by Chopin, and that was that, my life, what I understood of it, my lonely father, my distant older brother, my beautiful displaced Hungarian soulmate who appeared to want nothing more from this life than raising someone else's child, and me.

* * *

How much of his circumstances the child fails to question. Why, of all the Window Shop girls, had the most beautiful one not attracted a beau, a husband? Why did she so rarely go out on her nights off? What did they talk about, my father and Magda, in passing in the course of the day, or in those occasional times that she stayed in the kitchen to teach him some Eastern European dish or delicacy? All business, raising the child, the proper amount of paprika? What kept her with us, and why, to get ahead of the story, didn't she leave a note for me, to explain herself to me, to say goodbye when she left?

In the fall of 1956, the year of the Hungarian revolution, I was sent away to prep school in New Hampshire, the school Teddy had gone to. As it turned out, he had been a soccer star and the captain of the hockey team; my mother, one of few things I knew about her and one of the many things about her I seem not to have inherited, had been a near-Olympic figure skater. On the basis of his lingering reputation I was assigned without tryout and with fanfare to the first soccer team, and then quietly demoted to the third a week later. My room was a cubicle in a dormitory with twenty other cubicles, and from morning to night I was teased by the worldly boys from Oyster Bay and Tuxedo Park. I was miserably homesick and wrote Magda every week, letters filled with perhaps the most desperate longing I have ever felt. Her letters back to me, in her Old World idiom, were bathed in love: she "embraced me tenderly" every night; she believed "her young man" would "make A in all his studies"; in closing, she begged me "to remember her sweetest affections," and reminded me to wear my scarf and my galoshes. Then, in November, came a thicker envelope addressed in my father's unfamiliar scrawl, and in it was the last letter I had written Magda, unopened, and a note from him explaining that as Magda now had "no function in the household," he regretted to say that she had been "sent away."

For Christmas vacation I traveled back to Boston with a group of boys under the care of a master named Mr. Fortune, and as the train wound down through the backdrop of shabby mill towns and derelict backyards, I pretended, hoped, came to believe that, as for the next three weeks Magda would once again have a function in the household, it would be she meeting me at North Station. Once our group had been moved well clear of the tracks, the boys began to be picked off, with shouts, with hugs, by parents and siblings, and quite soon it was just me and Mr. Fortune standing alone in the center of all that holiday bustle. At last Mr. George, who had been waiting all this time in his Chevrolet at the curb, came forward. He gave his single name, which matched the name on Mr. Fortune's list of those authorized to take his charges off his hands, and with that Mr. Fortune was freed of my woes, and I was on my way, wordlessly, miserably, home.

When I arrived Donnie met me with thanks to Mary Mother of Jesus—she was always thanking Mary Mother of Jesus—for my safe return, but she was not the person I wanted to see. She tried to explain that my father was administering exams that afternoon but looked forward to dining with me that evening, but I ran past her and went up to my room, with the last hope or delusion that there might be a note for me from Magda. The surfaces of my curly maple bedroom set were bare, my pillow unsoftened, the scent only of Butcher's furniture polish. I ran upstairs to the third floor, to her room, which had never been cluttered with things— she didn't have a lot of things—but when I saw that the wedding photograph of her parents, the etching of the Danube flowing through Budapest, the official sanctified portrait of Cardinal Mindszenty, her brush and comb, that everything of her was gone and that this room now looked like exactly what it was, a bare unoccupied maid's quarter, I knew that I would never see her again, and I lay down on her bed and cried.

My father found me there, asleep, early in the evening. He had a sandwich and glass of milk on a tray for me. He put the tray on the top of the bureau and sat down at the end of the bed. For a month and a half I had hated him for sending her away, had planned several strategies of hurt and revenge upon him, but as we sat without speaking for a minute or two, I knew I wouldn't follow through on any of it. He was now the only family I had, and besides, after three months away he looked old to me, sitting there, tired, so hopeless confronting me that I let most of that go in a second. I sat up in the bed, pulled the pillow behind my back, and leaned against the chipped iron headboard. Why were you so mean? I asked. Why did you send her away? I'm sorry I said it that way, he answered. I just wanted you to know what was happening. I'm sorry she's gone, he continued. I miss her, too. But then why, I said, did she have to leave? Couldn't she have just lived with us, gone back to her job at the Window Shop, stayed here in this room that no one was going to need ever again? He sighed, one of those long breathy utterances that mean there is much about the world that a child, or anyone, can never understand. At last he told me that it wouldn't have been appropriate, a young woman and a man living unrelated in the same house. Magda and I agreed, he said, that it wasn't... and here he stopped saying what he was in the process of saying, and instead spent several ticks of the clock searching his English scholar's brain for a new word, but then simply settled back to what he had already said. It wouldn't be appropriate, you can see that. I really couldn't see it, but I tried to respond on his terms and gave voice, without planning, to the deepest truth in my soul. Then why not get married, I said. It would be perfect. She loves me, she loves the house. Why not?

My father could have answered that question in many different ways, any one of which would have saved me some small amount of grief in the years to come. In fact, I recognize now that he revealed more than he intended, and I was simply too young, too upset, too focused on my own grief to pick up on it. It didn't work like that, he said. So my memory tells me now. What I heard then was, It *doesn't* work like that, a dictum drawn forth from the opaque and immutable world of adulthood. My father patted my knee, stood up, pointed to my dinner on the tray, and left me in Magda's room. The white crotchet bedspread had become tangled around me, and after he left I drew it over my head, intending to cry some more. But tears didn't come, and in that starry darkness I determined that there was no way for me now but simply to grow up, to hasten age, to leave all this behind. In other words, lying there huddled pathetically in my old nanny's bed, I decided that if my father wouldn't marry her and bring her back to me, I'd have to marry her myself.

I spent that night in Magda's room, and spent the subsequent days of that vacation moving up there for good, my clothes, my record player, my collections of comic books and stamps, took over the entire warren of maid's quarters and closets under the eaves of the third floor, and in time it became the sort of spread that any teenager, and any teenager's friends, dream about. The next day I woke up late, went down to take my breakfast from Donnie sullenly. After I ate I put on my pea coat and plaid scarf—it was arctic cold that Christmas; it was always cold in December in the fifties—and set off down Brattle Street to Harvard Square. With the cold in New England always came brilliant crystal air and a bright, brave sun, and those great mansions, decked out for the holiday, sparkled in the snow. A girl named Lizzie Baker lived in one of them, and as I passed she was getting into her car with her parents, and I nearly had the courage to walk up their path to say hello. I had played with her a good bit growing up, as her nanny was a friend of Magda's. From my concealed vantage point behind all my layers of winter clothes, I was free to stare at her and feel the unfamiliar jolt of desire. I had not yet reached puberty, but it was drawing closer and arrived one night, to my astonishment, in my bed in my cubicle a few months later.

The Window Shop had moved by then from its tiny quarters on Mt. Auburn Street to its larger space on Brattle on the edge of the Square. The streets were packed with Christmas shoppers, and the Window Shop itself was almost too crowded for me to get in. I took a place in the line and was pressed forward, and at length it was my turn to be helped. It had been a long time since Magda's friends had worked there, and the counter girls were American teenagers, and had no patience for me as I stood stammering in front of the cases, thinking that I would at least buy a single cookie if I had any money in my pocket, which I didn't. I was ready to give up when one of the women in back, one of the original Austrian countesses who had founded the place, noticed me and came forward to take over. I had always been afraid of this imperious Teutonic figure, with her severe gray Austrian braids and large frightening bosom. She called me, unsmiling, and told me to come back into the kitchen with her. She barked a few commands in German to her browbeaten bakers, and then led me to a small office behind the refrigerators.

I never knew this woman's name, and I'm not entirely sure now what her motives were, but it was clear to me that she was taking valuable time out of her busiest days to talk to me. What can I tell you? she asked me. I made up a story about having a Christmas present to deliver to Magda; I was trying to sound adult, like a suitor. Not possible, she said, with a little surprise in her voice, recognizing that I had been told nothing. Why, I said. I want to see her. I need to see her. I was no longer trying to sound like anything but a child with a broken heart. Magda is in Austria, she said. Austria! So my project to woo and win her, even that silly pre-adolescent fantasy, was denied to me. The blows to my hopes would never cease. What is she doing there? I asked. She narrowed her eyes, accusing me in advance of being a typically ignorant American with no knowledge of world affairs, and asked if I knew what was going on in Hungary. As a matter of fact I did know what was going on; in my isolation at school I had taken to spending free hours in the library reading *The New York Times*. All fall I'd read the news stories coming out of Hungary, seen the photos of Soviet tanks in Budapest, the pictures of Hungarian Freedom Fighters not much older than me launching Molotov cocktails. Hungary was a home to me, and Imre Nagy was my hero, Janos Kadar my nemesis. Yes, I said, I know what is going on in Hungary.

For a few moments her tone softened with me. She was worried about Magda, who, she told me, had gone back to Austria to see if she could get her parents out. People were being shot at the border. I knew that. She tried to reassure me, and herself, that all would be well; Magda had a network of places to stay, her extended Austro-Hungarian family, the friends and distant relations of all the women who worked at the shop. She had a little money, even, which would come in useful at the border, and this woman asked me if I knew where that money had come from. Since I hadn't known anything about all this it was an odd question, but it was rhetorical: my father, she told me, had paid for all this. What did I think of that? she asked. Well, I said, that was nice of him. I expected her to agree, to say that it was not merely nice, but generous and noble, to tell me perhaps what a great man my father was. Not at all. Her tone hardened up once more, became bitter. It was the least he could have done, she snapped. All those years wasted. They'd tried to talk sense to her. But no, she was led on. Awful. With that, I was dismissed.

What could I have made of this, all these references to things I didn't know about and all these accusations for wrongs I hadn't committed? I squeezed my way back out of the shop, and landed once again on Brattle Street, feeling as if I had been whipped. I knew she was talking about love, but whose? The only love I cared about at that moment was my own. Of all the things this woman had said to me, what hurt most was her saying that Magda's time with us, raising me, bathing me, teaching me, mothering me, had been wasted. I walked the gay streets of Harvard Square dazed. In my whole life, late child in what may have been an arid marriage, delayed cause—for all I knew—of my mother's early death, I had never felt more unwanted.

But the heart, which so often makes us miserable and stupid, once in a while shows us a truth that can withstand the most withering test. So this is what my heart told me on the streets of Cambridge that day. Whatever the mysteries that were now spiraling around me, whatever the true story that had been occupying my life like dark matter, unseen and unproven, Magda loved me. This was certain; I knew that in response to any conceivable piece of evidence to the contrary, it would only become more certain, and true; it would persist. On that foundation, in months and years to come, I built a whole person, a boy who returned to school and slowly, over the months and years, outlasted sarcasm, finessed his athletic deficiencies, and earned friendship; a young man who went to college and won success when he was willing to work for it; and an adult who has gone through life making only the requisite number of mistakes and achieving no more and no less than he deserved.

Teddy did not come home for Christmas that year, a fact that seemed understandable. My father had told me he was starting training in a bank in New York. My father said nothing more about this, but Donnie did, shedding a tear thinking, out loud, how lonely it seemed, just my father and me in this big house. A few months earlier I might have felt the same way, but much had changed for me. I was growing up, and the events with my father were drawing us closer. I had learned, at last, that he was not one who could volunteer much, that things that mattered to him or hurt him came out as stiff technicalities, like telling me that Magda had been "sent away." I had told him that I knew she was in Austria, and he was relieved to have it out in the open. Side by side each morning we combed *The Boston Herald* and *The New York Times* for news about the Revolution. He did not try to hide how worried he was for her, how much he cared, and on this ground we met as equals. Over a hundred thousand refugees had streamed across the border, and in that crush it seemed possible would be Magda's family, but it was still many months before any of us heard something for certain.

For Christmas that year I gave my father a pair of tiger-striped socks, with felt claws sewn on the tips of the toes. I can't imagine how I came to choose them, but he delighted me by taking off his own shoes and socks—I had never before seen my father's bare feet—and by wearing my present for the rest of the day. He gave me a set of stainless-steel tools, a selection of bits with a common handle, a tiny hammer, a fierce-looking saw blade; they all came in a zippered leather case with my initials embossed on it. Less successfully, he gave me a selection of Milton's *Poetical Works*, but I have both these gifts with me today, though I have lost the Phillips head bit along the way. Its empty spot, still patiently waiting for the return after all these years, seems just right to me. For our dinner, as usual, he had roasted a goose. He apologized that there were raisins in the stuffing because he knew I didn't like them, but pointed out the juice from them gave the breast meat a fine, fruity tang. After our meal we took a walk through the streets, and he told me stories about the families in, it seemed, every house between ours and Harvard Yard.

I have said that Magda had left no goodbyes for me, and that is technically the truth. But when we came back from our walk there was one more present under the tree. My father pointed it out as if magic had left it there. It was a pair of mittens. I'm unable to say anything more about them, but I will say this: in fifty years, she has never missed a Christmas present for me.

I must now move on to Teddy, who, like my lost screwdriver bit, has left an empty place in this story. When the Christmas vacation was over, Mr. George was again enlisted to drive me to North Station, and Mr. Fortune was once again there to transport the boys back up north, and I went back to my Latin and algebra, and when the hockey team assignments were posted I was not surprised, relieved, really, to see that the former captain's brother was assigned to the lowest club team, the seventh, in fact. Everyone at that school played hockey, except for the handful that boxed. In the spring I rowed. I forget what number boat I was in, but it was also the lowest. But for all that, my bed was not short-sheeted again, my shoelaces were not tied into knots, people got bored of calling me Skeesix on account of my hair, I won a place on the debating team, and I finished the year in a better place than I had begun it.

For the summer I was sent to a riding camp at the base of the Teton Mountains in Wyoming, and this was such an expensive, exclusive though deliberately rustic summer camp that all of the fifteen or so boys in it were oddballs just like me: only children of the presidents of Fortune 50 corporations, Jewish sons who arrived with twelve classics they had to read and summarize in weekly letters to their fathers, orphans who would be millionaires on their twenty-first birthdays. We got along famously, learned to ride, and were hardened by a three-week pack trip into complete wilderness. When we returned we were greeted by the fifteen girls that would now take over the facilities, and in that one-week overlap between sessions I fell in love for the first time, a girl named Jeannie Park, who I never saw again.

All this time, with me now back at school and a little-used sub on the second soccer team, Teddy hovered around me. His Dink Stover legend had begun to crack as my success in every subject but math led more than one master to remark that I was indeed not my brother's brother, that he had been, as one of the masters put it, "not the brightest lamppost in the park." I had gotten used to his careless smirk shining out from the center of champion team portraits, but in those other archived relics of prep school life, the newspaper staff portrait, the literary club banquet, the cast of Julius Caesar, if he was in those pictures at all, he was in the back row, carrying a spear. It's a good moment in youth, when one discovers that there is room at the top with, or perhaps even beyond, one's unassailable older siblings, a good moment whether the siblings are loved, or not.

So as yet another Christmas, in 1957, went by without his presence, and I began to measure the time since I had seen him in years, it began to dawn on me that this was a rather unusual state of affairs. I asked my father about him over the holidays, and he answered as if there was nothing so odd about it, that he was an adult with his own life, that my father had had dinner with him not so long ago when he was down in the city, that in any event with him so much older than me, and with my mother's death putting an end to normal family life, there wasn't much else that could have been expected. With that, I went back to school, made the fourth hockey team and the fifth crew, won the Latin Prize, and the summer was again upon me.

I was fifteen by then. Magda had been gone from me for almost two years. She had written that her parents and sister had escaped, and they were all living with relatives in Austria. Had she married, started her own family? There was nothing of that in my Christmas note, and my father insisted that he had heard nothing, and if his conduit for news was the woman at the Window Shop, he was lucky to hear what he did. Fifteen is an awkward age in the summer, and I spent it in Cambridge, taking piano lessons at the Longy School of Music, spending the afternoon with my friend Danny at triple features in the seedy movie halls of Boston's lower Washington Street, entertaining my old friend Lizzie and her Winsor School classmates in my private spaces on the third floor. My father had given me a hi-fi for Christmas, and we played Elvis and Everly Brothers records. But somewhere in July it occurred to me that I might go to New York, that I might go by myself on the train and spend a few days with my brother. My father said no, the kind of flat no that does nothing but inspire questions. Why not? I asked. He's my brother, isn't he? Yes, said my father, and he added, in a way that made it clear he would do nothing of the sort, Perhaps we'll see if he'd like to come up and spend Labor Day with us. After all this time I finally recognized that there was something truly creepy going on here, and I blurted out a question that had never before been on my mind: What happened between you? Happened? asked my father. Happened, I said. There was no "rift" between them, he said. He's a grown man living his own life.

Back to school for my junior year, and in order to avoid soccer altogether I was a volunteer aide in the state mental hospital, a missionary activity one could do in this very Episcopalian school in lieu of one sport a year, and another prize at the end of the year, this one in French, and a summer in Cambridge with a barely paid job as a patient sitter in McLean's mental hospital in Belmont, and a senior year in which sports became, if not an elective, then at least quite easily ducked, and there I was, for the opening days of Christmas of 1959, in New York going to parties with those very same worldly boys from Oyster Bay and Tuxedo Park who had long ago been so mean to me. They'd taken to calling me Skeesix again, or more commonly, "Skeez," but now it was cool.

I had once copied down Teddy's telephone number from my father's address book, and one early evening, after about an hour of false starts, I called him up. He answered, and I introduced myself, giving my name, and adding "your brother" as a helpful reminder. There was a pause, then, Hey, how about that, my little brother on his own in New York, what's up? Well, I said, I was here for a few days, and I was wondering whether, maybe, he wanted to get together with me. Another pause, and then an audible shrug. Sure, he said, how about we grab a hamburger tomorrow night? He gave me an address not far from where I was staying. We'd meet at seven.

The place he had selected was a bar, long and deep, with the bar and stools running front to back on one side, and high-backed booths running along the other. The wood of all the features was dark and shiny with use, and the tin ceiling, high above, was water-stained and looked a little insecure. There was a neon Schlitz sign in the window, a pile of ruffled newspapers at one end of the bar, a bartender who looked about my father's age and at least a hundred pounds heavier. It was one of those unpretentious neighborhood pubs that have long been superseded by upscale establishments designed to look like what they had replaced. There were a couple of men in suits and ties at the bar, and they glanced at me in a not unfriendly way when I walked in. The drinking age in New York in those days was eighteen, and though I wasn't yet of age I looked plausibly legal, and the bartender asked me what I wanted. A Schlitz, I said, and he shrugged off his own inner impulse to ask me for ID, poured me my beer, and when I asked, told me I could sit in any booth I liked. I felt pretty good, actually; I thought to myself, This is okay, me, New York, my own beer, my brother.

He arrived about twenty minutes late. He was even more handsome, more flawless than I remembered, which meant he had indeed inherited our mother's sharp beauty. He moved like a jock, a slight swagger, dexterous; even standing still he seemed to lay claim to the space around him, like the hockey defenseman he had once been. The tailors at Brooks Brothers must have loved him; his body could have made secondhand rags look good. I stood up, shook his hand, let him make his remarks about how I'd grown, et cetera. We sat, and he apologized for being late. A rough day at the office, he said. I stopped off for a shooter with my friends to unwind. That's fine, I said, I'm catching up, and raised my glass rather self-consciously as a toast of sorts. He called out for a martini, very dry, he added, which was what our father always said.

So, how many years has it been? he asked. Four, I said. Christmas of 1955. Yeah, that's right. Phew. I haven't been back to Cambridge in four years. So what's up with the old man? he asked. Throwing the rule book at you, is he? In my life with my father I had been subject to no rules whatsoever. Still, I told Teddy he was fine, getting ready to retire from teaching, that Garland, in fact, seemed to be on its last legs, anyway. What a dump, my brother said. I never did figure why he worked there. Why not Harvard, for Christ's sake? We'd been talking for five minutes, and already I was beginning to regret this. It's just what worked out for him, I answered. It was the Depression, remember? Jobs were hard to get, and he took the one he could find. Yeah, well, the Depression didn't wing him at all. He had the money stashed under his mattress, I guess. Still there, for all I see of it. I answered that I didn't know anything about his money, but that in any event, he didn't spend a dime of it on himself.

We had exhausted most of our common ground. He loudly ordered another drink for himself, and another beer for me, which I didn't want, and purely as a way to gain some time, or something, I got up to go to the bathroom. I didn't have to go, just stood in the men's room looking at myself in the mirror, asking my young and ungainly face how it was that this man was my brother. What I was asking my reflected self was not just why were we so different in manner, or appearance and skills, but why our stories were so different, why our truths about a common past seemed to bear no relationship. My father as a character in his story—a tight-fisted tyrant—was not the socially awkward but kind-hearted person he would have been in mine.

I went back to my seat, and like a cartoon drunk who feels he's been left too long, he asked if I'd gone to the storeroom and found a little nooky. I laughed, sort of. Speaking of nooky, he said, whatever happened to that girl, that Polish chick that had worked for us, Maya, was that her name? All an act, I knew it, but for the last time, I played along. Hungarian, I said. Her name was Magda.

Magda, right. I fucked her, you know. God, every vacation for a few years there we did it like bunnies. She had that whole third floor, and you were asleep, and the old man was down there cooking up his epi-cure-ean dee-lights, and Magda and I were up in her room with her skinny Hungarian ass in the air. Oh, excuse me. She was your nanny or something. Let's say Magda and I were up in her room having intimate relations. The old man never had a clue. It was great. Fact is, I could use a little of that right about now. See, though, the problem was she thought she was in love with me, she wanted to get married. I told her sure, we'd get married someday, but I'll tell you, that got old real fast. But you want to know the really funny thing about all this? Guess who had his own designs. You can't guess? No? Okay, it was the old man. Can you dig it? He must have been something like thirty years older than she was, an English professor at some third-rate podunk college, and he thought this absolute babe would marry him. Want to know how I know that? No? Well, I'll tell you, anyway. He asked me whether I would object, kind of a Dickens thing, him inviting me into his office, asking me to sit down. Christ, I thought the old guy was going get down on his knee and propose to me. Not amused? Come on, you're a stiff one, aren't you? Playing hockey? No? Did you know I was the captain of the team at school? Played some in college, but Christ, too much hassle. Well, it was getting a little weird here, me screwing the girl my father wants to marry. I don't know if he ever found out, but I sure wasn't going to stick around. Besides, I was getting bored of the whole thing. This was when, the year I graduated, or no, my first year here in New York. You must have been, like, in sixth grade or something. How old are you? You don't know how old you are? Hey, barkeep, cut this kid off. So anyway, those last few visits there were pretty dicey, and I wasn't even getting laid anymore. Question is: did you ever know about this, ever hear anything from upstairs? I guess you were a little young. But still you know, she hung around hoping I'd change my mind, or something. Phew. Family stories, right?

I didn't know exactly what to do when Teddy finished. There was no point in talking anymore, and it was time, anyway, to rejoin my friends for another party. I met the girl who became my first wife that night, and even if the marriage could not last, I have no regrets. It only seemed to me, sitting in that bar in Manhattan, that I should hold on to what I believed was the truth. I got up, fished in my pocket, and threw down a couple of dollars. Hey, he said, not staying for a burger? No, I said. I started to walk away, but then came back. One thing I'll tell you. She didn't stay for you, or our father, that's what no one understands about this story. She didn't stay in that house waiting for you to marry her, you sorry piece of shit, she stayed for me.

When I reflect on that parting shot with my brother, Teddy, I see my young self in a moment of glory. I became an adult that evening, if memory serves, but I wonder if it really happened like that. Memory, after all, is the product of desire, how we wish, or fear, things had gone before "truth...with all her matter of fact" (Mr. Saunders, seventh-grade English) is allowed to intrude. "You sorry piece of shit," I said, but I can't think of a single other time in my life that I used the word "sorry" as in "regrettable or deplorable." Nothing I knew or remembered about Teddy squares with that coarse drunk I saw that evening, not that I ever forgave him. We see, in the end, what we need to see.

Years later, in celebration, I think, of my return home from the Peace Corps in Nepal, my father took me to dinner at Locke-Ober. We were shown up the narrow stairs in that rickety building to the musty corridor of private dining rooms, and we were taken to the smallest, the most intimate, a threadbare couch along the wall, a table set for two with a single rose in a bud vase. We sat down, ordered everything from turtle soup to baked Alaska. The truth is, he whispered to me, the food here isn't very good, but the wine cellar is superb. He knew what he was after, and our bottles were brought with considerable ceremony, including the painstaking decanting of the Bordeaux for the lamb.

I don't really know why, but at the end of the meal, sated, stuffed, smoking cigars, I asked him, Pop, why do you think Magda stayed with us all that time? I might have expected him to avoid answering—what an impossible question, anyway—but he took it up as if he had been waiting years for me to ask it, as if he needed this chance to set the record straight. Oh, he said, there's not much doubt about that. It was Teddy, of course. She was in love with him. Yes, I said, it's the only thing that makes sense. I took a few more puffs of my cigar, and then asked, But what does sense have to do with it? He smiled. Perhaps not all that much, he said.

Magda is still living in Austria, in Graz. She was eighteen when she landed in America, and twenty-eight when she left, and she resumed her life quickly once back in Europe. Her husband is retired from his teaching career at the ancient university where Kepler formulated his three laws and where, hundreds of years later, Schrödinger discovered his cat. She has grandchildren, and I imagine that the small gift she sends to me at Christmas—an ornament for my tree, a box of chocolates—is one of dozens of little packages she sends, some of them to the addresses of her youth. I can't imagine that her time in America, those years she worked as a nanny in a big house in Cambridge where three males blindly vied for her favor, is ever that much on her mind. If she thinks back fondly, I suspect it is to her friends at the Window Shop, sitting together behind the counter, gazing through the high shop windows at their futures in front of them.

And We Will Be Here

E ach day she woke before dawn and walked the grounds of the American hospital. She didn't go far. She kept to the footpaths that encircled the main hall, past the evergreens and the timber cottages now used as additional wards for the wounded.

It had once been a Japanese vocational school for the arts, and she remembered the painter who had asked her and Junpei to model. They had been walking past the school that afternoon, and the young man had called to them. He led them under the gate and to a tree, where she sat with Junpei between her legs. She pretended to read to her companion, though it wasn't a book she held. The painter had instead given her his hat and told her to imagine. It was made of wool and smelled of sweat and pine, and the band inside of it had worn away so that strands of it fell onto her wrist. She had never been inside the school until then, though passed it often and would later wonder behind which window the painter lived. A wind blew, and the shadow of leaves swam across their arms. They kept still. Beside them was a stone garden. She never saw the young man again.

Her name was Miya, and twenty-five years had passed since that day, though lately she found herself thinking about the painter as she took her walks around the hospital. Or not him exactly, but the painting, which she never saw finished. Perhaps it had hung someplace in the school's corridors. Or in someone's home or even at a museum, she thought, when she was feeling fanciful. Perhaps he had become famous, and she was unaware of it. She wondered how many people had seen their image there, under that tree, and how many questioned who the children were, if they did at all.

She did not own any childhood photographs of herself and did not have anyone to tell her what she looked like then. She believed she was now thirty-four years old but wasn't certain. There wasn't anyone to tell her about that, either. She had been born in Japan, she knew, and had come here to Korea at an early age, to this island south of the peninsula. But she had no memory of this journey or any time before that. Hers was a life adapted, she would have said, if someone asked.

The woman who raised her had passed away from sickness. Miya had brought her to the hospital, and she remembered this as well, their kindness, Miss Hara among the soldiers. They had liked Miss Hara, and a group of doctors once sang for her while she was dying. It was an American song. Barbershop, someone said, and she didn't know what that meant. Miss Hara smiled at them and gripped the footboard with her toes. This was two years ago.

She didn't know then that she would leave the orphanage and return to this place, assisting the nurses with the wounded. A volunteer, the doctor named Henry suggested, and she thought it a fine word. He was tall with freckled skin and a broad forehead. "Help is always needed," he said, and escorted her inside. On that first day he gave her a hospital gown, and she was puzzled. He shrugged, embarrassed. They were low on supplies. The gowns were comfortable, he said, and even provided her with a nurse's cap so everyone could tell her apart from the others.

Every day she brought the soldiers water. She trimmed their hair if it tickled their ears. She scratched their backs. She made them fresh lemonade from the citrus grove. She spoke to them if conversation was what they desired. She wheeled them out of the wards for a bit of air. She worked until her body grew numb. A thousand beds and convalescents scattered throughout the buildings.

"What's your name?" she always asked. "Where are you from?" Australia, someone said. Another: Greece. She had met men from France, New Zealand, Thailand, America, and the peninsula. With every new arrival she searched their faces, pushing the gurney or the wheelchair through the corridors. A man's nose reminded her of someone she once knew. Someone else's lips curved downward the way hers did. She found the eyes of Miss Hara. Junpei's chin. The familiar touch of skin. A scar on the elbow.

I knew you once, she would think, moving through the wards as if she had done so all her life.

Her own room was on the second floor of the main hall, and when she wasn't occupied with a patient or when Henry told her to rest, she retired there. It wasn't much: a single bed, a desk

beside a window. The walls were bare. She owned few posses-
sions. She had a teacup and a comb, an extra set of clothes, and a
sewing machine, all taken from the orphanage. The sewing
machine she placed atop the desk, which had a drawing of what
she guessed to be continents.

She sewed old gowns and on occasion a soldier's uniform if it
could be saved. She sipped water from the teacup, for she wasn't
sure if she could ask for tea. She kept the door closed. A bare light
bulb hung from the ceiling, casting a dome around her. Finished
with the clothes, she would study the landmasses on the desk,
done in thick paint, the texture of it rising in places like topogra-
phy. Who did it or how long it had been there she didn't know.
With her finger she traced the outlines of her imagined nations
until sleep came to her and she lay on her bed and shut her eyes
and felt the satisfaction of a day fulfilled.

These were her days. In their patterns she found comfort. And
every morning, before dawn, she rose and walked outside, following the footpaths as one would a map. In two years, she hadn't
once left the hospital property. Instead, she kept watch over the
grounds like a sentry, pacing within its border.

On some days she climbed the tree beside the stone garden.
From this distance she could see the campus in its intended sym-
metry. The main hall at the center. Its roof of red tiles, weather-
worn, the eaves that shaded the stucco walls. The patio and the
courtyard. The citrus grove and the hills. The coastal mountains,
their peaks covered in the remnants of last month's snow. The
color of the land muted.

None of it had changed, was what she concluded on these
mornings. Any moment now the students would appear from the
main hall, as they used to, she herself standing on the other side
of the fence. She thought this and waited for the sun to rise, her
arms hooked around a branch, her legs dangling, the world, it
seemed, not yet awake. The war was far.

And it was here one morning, up in the tree, that she witnessed
the cargo trucks coming down the main road. She had grown accustomed to them, of course, but with every visit she felt her heart
against her chest and remained motionless. Headlights crowned
the hill. There was the low pitch of a radio. She heard a woman's
voice, singing, accompanied by a brass band that seemed to float

across the fields, caught by the winds. The trucks grew closer, rumbling. In their approach they resembled elephants. Dust sprayed underneath their wheels. They turned into the driveway and parked in the courtyard, their engines idle, their headlights sweeping across the field.

All at once men stumbled out of the cargo hold, their bodies shadowed, scurrying like thieves. The air was violet, and their movements were black. Some knelt on the grass and appeared to be digging. The air popped, and then the grass caught fire, first in one corner, then in another, and another, as if the ground had cracked open to illuminate the stretchers, dozens of them, already spread out on the lawn.

Miya climbed down the tree and brushed away dirt from her hospital gown. She tucked the loose strands of her hair behind her ears and put on her nurse's cap. She followed the path to the driveway, engulfed by the smoke of flares and the scent of the wounded. She joined a nurse and lifted a stretcher, shocked by the soldier's lightness. He was an American. His gaze lolled, and his breath was sour. The nurse led them past the doors and into the main hall.

"What's your name?" Miya asked the soldier. "Where are you from?"

He looked up at her, seeing her upside down. He grinned. "Hi, doll face," he said. "I'm Benson from Boston."

"Hello, Benson from Boston," she said, and the American blinked, and his smile vanished. When he was settled into a bed she took his hand.

Soon after, a patient was placed on the bed beside Benson's. She didn't go to him until later, curious, parting the curtain to reveal a young man with gauze wrapped around his head and bandages over his eyes. He was a mainlander, perhaps. Or an island native. He was comatose, she realized, and asked Benson whether he knew who the patient was. Benson didn't respond, staring up at the ceiling as he would for most of his time here. She checked to see if Henry was close by. He was at the end of the ward. She turned again toward the bandaged patient and shut the curtain behind her.

She leaned forward. It was as though layers of his body had been stripped. "Hello," she whispered, not yet recognizing him. The sun had risen, and the ward blazed white for a moment before the clouds passed. She lifted the bandages away from his eyes and almost at once drew her hand back as if stung. She looked around, disoriented, clutching the bed sheet. She knew him, she kept repeating. She knew him, though no one responded. He was there, within this face, this aged body, she was certain of it. But her voice had failed her, and so she spoke in silence about how long it had been and how he had come back, as she knew he would, this boy, whom she held under a tree, many years ago, while a man painted their likeness.

She was woken by the fading thunder of aircraft. Then almost at once the quiet returned. She was unsure of the time. Her eyes adjusted to the faint light from the windows, the convalescents lined up along the walls like dark monuments. She had fallen asleep on a chair beside Junpei's bed.

Benson was muttering, "I didn't do nothing. I didn't do nothing at all." She crossed over to him and massaged his temples with her fingertips. He was sweating. A fever. She went to the sink and soaked a cloth in cold water and then returned to drape it over Benson's forehead. A nurse shuttled past her, yawning. "Get some sleep, Miya," she whispered, waving her hand in the air, and headed to the quarters. Miya put on her coat. And then, looking back at Junpei once more, his shadowed body under a sheet, she stepped outside to breathe in the air.

At the stone garden she sat on the bench and took off her shoes. The garden's terrain was made of sand, raked to resemble currents of water running beside the stones. She placed her feet into the sand and felt the coolness of it and then the quick warmth, as though the earth were a hand tugging at her ankles. She looked up at the tree and then shut her eyes and drifted into sleep once more, the empty windows of the hospital shadowing her shoulders.

In daylight she rose to the footsteps of convalescents and nurses. At the grove she plucked a lemon, slipping it into her pocket before returning inside. Junpei lay with his arms to his side. She leaned forward and inhaled his raspy breath and saw the child she remembered still there along the bottom half of his face. She brought the lemon to her mouth and bit into the rind, breaking away the flesh. She squeezed the juice onto a wet cloth and began to clean his chin, wiping away dirt and crusted blood.

"You'll need a proper bath, soon," she said. "Like everyone else here. It's no longer a school, you know. But there is still the tree. And the stone garden. Of course there is."

They had found him beside the remnants of a house, she was told. "He wouldn't have gone inside first," Henry said, examining his legs. "We'd have nothing left of him if he did."

She ran her fingers over his bandages, guessing where his eyebrows were hidden. "Where have you been, Junpei?" she asked him, cleaning his hands.

She had witnessed his first step, she recalled. At the orphanage's entrance. Once learned, he walked all throughout the day, the child's face filled with determination as he swayed his hips and his arms, shuffling from the dormitory to the barn and out to the fences. "Messenger," they called him, watching the boy charge with fury to nowhere in particular, past the other children, who paused and watched him with bemusement.

The orphanage was still there, she knew, on the other side of the western hills. It had expanded over the years, housing children from the war. She didn't go to it anymore.

She and Junpei had arrived at the same time. An earthquake had destroyed Tokyo. They had, along with hundreds of others, been airlifted to this island, which was under Japanese rule then. Cheju, it was called. Their ages were guessed. Names were given. They had not known each other before. They were paired together and slept on a blanket on the floor, her arm tucked under his head. They lay on their sides, facing each other, their bodies in the shape of prayer. Junpei's hair caught in her teeth when she woke in the mornings.

In those early years she bathed him. She filled unused fuel barrels with water and lifted the boy into it. He would cling to her ears as she washed his chest. Old enough, she brought Junpei to Miss Hara's lessons, learning both Japanese and the Korean dialect of the island. They were taught songs. Mathematics as well. They helped with the house chores, wiping windows with newspaper, mopping the floors, taking breaks to duel with brooms in the yard. They took walks through the forest and up the hills to view the ocean and down towards the school. Not once did they speak of Tokyo.

When the boy was nearly Miya's height, Miss Hara asked him

whether he now preferred to stay with the other boys. He shook his head, clutching Miya's hand, and she felt the surety of his grip and was convinced in that moment that they would grow old together. That theirs was a shared life. She would, at night, tell him of this. A house by the sea. They would fish. They would plant a garden. "Ponies," she would add, facing him, her fingers galloping across his shoulders lit by the moon.

She would always remember that morning when he left her in the yard to chase a crow. In memory there was his face and only that, the open mouth, his wet eyes, his return, his hands picking at his clothes, an animal-like cry erupting from the center of his body. How he held her, and she, unable to calm him, saw Miss Hara hurrying towards the barn. Miya followed. A crowd had formed. They were all looking up.

It took her a moment to realize that what hung from the rafters was in fact a person and not a doll, his limbs dangling, as if filled with cotton. It was a boy, his face discolored from the rope around his neck. And there was Junpei, beside her, clutching her waist, pointing at the floor where a shoe had fallen. No one else noticed.

It wasn't long after this that Junpei began to leave. She would wake to find that he had already risen. Or on other days she would be washing clothes and turn to see that he was no longer there. In the evenings he didn't show up for supper. She searched the dormitory and the classrooms. She ran down the road and saw at last his figure in the distance, standing there, his hands rooted into his pockets.

"Junpei," she called one evening, taking hold of his wrist. "Where have you been?"

It was growing dark. He wouldn't look at her, his eyes roaming over the mountains. "Not far," he said.

"Miss Hara will be worried," she said, tugging on his arm. "Come."

She turned, and he followed her. At the orphanage they slept as they always did.

That night he woke her with his voice. "I can't find it, Miya. I've looked everywhere. For the other one. He was barefoot, you know. I saw his toes."

In six months' time, Junpei was gone. They had been at the

orphanage for over a decade. It was the beginning of winter. Snow had yet to fall. She went to bathe. Upon her return, he had left. Miya, dressed in her nightgown, ran down the road and called his name and waited, her hair beginning to freeze. Miss Hara found her that afternoon, still waiting. With her hands she had torn the hem of her gown.

It was the year an American woman named Earhart had flown over the Pacific. From Hawaii to California. She recalled that she and Junpei had heard through the radio. That evening they climbed the hill behind the orphanage. They walked to the edge of the cliff. They raised their hands above their eyes and peered out at the horizon until the ocean faded.

All that week she remained beside him, vigilant. Benson ignored her, staring up at the ceiling. With her head resting on her hand she watched Junpei. The flat bridge of his nose. The curve of his cheekbones. His chapped lips. She dipped her finger in lemon water and placed it into his mouth, convinced that in his sleep it would sink into the soil of his tongue and he would dream of citrus. She felt his teeth, like crags, the one he had lost a mystery to her, this empty space near the front, an incomplete thought. The hair on his face was beginning to grow. He smelled of staleness and storage. She felt the calloused skin of his feet, wondering if any traces of where he had been remained there.

She spoke to him. Of her years. Of what he had missed. "You still have your youth," she told him. "You'll get used to things."

She attempted to imagine his own years away but couldn't. They were an indecipherable map, with nameless cities and towns, borderless countries. She saw him forever on a boat following the routes along the Pacific, absent of history, invisible to it. He would have woken one day in a cabin, feeling the ocean shudder, great spires of smoke in the far distance in Japan, as if the entire country were evaporating. He would not have thought of her then.

And would he have ever gone to Tokyo? She wasn't sure. She didn't think so. She never believed he had gone in search of that. Instead, he had fled. Sure of this, she fell asleep beside him, speaking of gardens to his silent face.

She was startled from a dream she couldn't remember. Carrying a lamp she wandered the hospital's corridors, as she did when she first arrived. In the hallways she brought the light up to the walls, expunging the moonlight. On first glance the walls were bare, nondescript, the paint yellowed by age and dust. The longer she stared, however, bright rectangular shapes rose out of them, spaced out evenly along the walls like ghost windows.

She had searched for paintings before. She used to ask Henry about them, but he shrugged, disinterested. All that night she looked again. First she explored the main hall, taking the staircase slowly. There were so many doors. She paused at each of them, listening to a patient's breathing. If she heard nothing, she slid the doors open and inspected the rooms now used to store equipment, cans of food, extra mattresses. She went outside and into the cottages, opening closets, waking the patients there, who looked at her perplexed. She brought a finger to her lips, as if sharing some kind of secret. She hunted with all that was left of her energy, releasing it in a great burst.

Exhausted, she headed towards the stone garden. The moon hung over the crest of the hills, an even light spreading over the grass, the trees, and the sand that shone like diamonds. Midway there she stopped. One of the stones had moved. She squinted, then rubbed her eyes with her palms, shaking her head, feeling her limbs grow heavy. The stone moved again. It rose. It began to approach her, and she clenched her fists, wondering to what world she had entered in these hours. Closer, it grew skin and then a face formed and she saw that it was a boy, no older than thirteen.

"Hey, miss," the boy said, in the island dialect. "I hear your footsteps. All over." He tapped his earlobes. He was dressed in dark pants, a button-down shirt, and rubber moccasins. His head was shaved, and he had thin lips. A small leather pouch hung from his belt loop. He asked what Miya was looking for.

"Paintings," Miya replied. "Seen any?"

Laughter erupted from the boy's small mouth. "I see nothing," he said, and motioned for her to step closer.

She did so, bending forward. The boy's eyes were fogged, like porcelain. He reached up to touch Miya's face, extending his fingers along her jaw line and then closing them over her nose. His hands smelled of cinnamon. He rose and took Miya's hand. "Come with me," he said, leading her to the stone garden.

Was he a patient? she asked. Another volunteer?

He didn't respond. He sat on the garden's edge and began to wipe the waves away in the sand until the surface was smooth. He opened his pouch and dug his fingers into it, lifting his hand to reveal dozens of marbles. These he placed in the middle of the sandbox, adjusting the cluster, each orb illuminating colors under the night sky. Satisfied, he offered a marble to Miya, who took it and lay on her stomach in the grass. She flicked her thumb and followed the marble's path over the surface of the sand as it ricocheted against the others. The boy lay down beside her. His hands rested on his chin, his legs swaying in the air.

"What does it look like?" the boy asked.

She turned onto her back. Stars formed into shapes and then broke apart. The blinking dot of an airplane. The silhouettes of branches. She used to wait for Junpei to return. She would climb trees at the orphanage, the ground below shrinking. The forest canopy opened to her like the waves of the sea, meeting the sky where a flock of birds rose out of it, spraying leaves. She waited for boats.

The boy nudged her, breathing into her ear, pointing at the marbles. "Hey, miss," he said, repeating his question.

"Fireworks," Miya responded.

The following morning the boy was gone. The day was warmer than the others. The sun had settled onto her skin. The ground was damp. When she rose from beside the garden she saw the land had created a cast of her body: grass folded pale to form her slightly parted legs, the curve of her shoulders, the sand indented where she had rested her head. Beside that was the shape of the boy, too, though it appeared he had been lying on his side, watching her. Or was it that? Her certainty, an instant before so sure, abandoned her. A wind came and stole the shapes. She looked for the marbles' paths, but they had been erased as well, replaced by the waves that were always there. The rake had been placed under the bench like an old rifle. She brushed sand from her hair.

Inside she found Henry tending to a soldier who was recovering from surgery. They were sending him to a rehabilitation clinic in Virginia, Henry told him. The soldier seemed pleased with the news. They shook hands. The doctor continued with his rounds.

She stood in the ward's entrance for a moment and watched the soldier sit up in bed suddenly, stretch forward, fingers extended, and touch the space where his legs had once been.

She approached Junpei's bed. If she stared at him long enough it seemed he wasn't breathing. Or as if the entire room was, rising and falling. Henry was beside her now, making note of Junpei's vitals. In his hand was the nurse's cap he had given to her. She must have dropped it somewhere.

"Junpei, you said his name was?" Henry asked, without looking at the chart.

"There was a boy," Miya said. "He is blind. A native. Have you seen him?"

Henry kept his gaze at her for a moment and then shook his head.

"Is he a volunteer?" she asked.

"Miya."

"He wore dark pants and moccasins. Perhaps he isn't a patient."

Henry looked over her shoulder, and she saw the tiredness of his skin. He took her arm and led her outside to the corridor. They stood by a window, and his pale hair speckled in daylight.

"He carries marbles. In a little pouch."

"Miya," Henry repeated. "You aren't sleeping." He spoke in a whisper. "We've talked about this. Do you remember? You're of no use to me if you aren't sleeping."

She took her cap and put it on.

"There are others you could tend to," he continued.

She ignored him. She had known Henry for two years now. He had been one of the singers when the orphanage director was here. She avoided his stare and returned to Junpei and his stillness. She placed lemon onto his lips and then combed his hair with her fingers. She had done the same for Miss Hara and spent the days reading to her from a book of folktales, keeping her company as the woman drifted in and out of consciousness.

"Has he been bathed?" she asked Henry. "It's time, I think. Don't you agree? We could remove the bandages, also. From his eyes. It can't be good for him. He would wake to see nothing."

In Henry's hand was a plastic cup filled with two tablets. "For your headache, Miya," he said.

Had she complained of that? She couldn't recall. She took the pills, slipping them under her tongue, and thanked him.

"Rest for an hour," he encouraged her. "You need your strength. Do you remember, Miya? Like we said. You need to rest."

He took her arm again and led her upstairs to her room. She didn't protest. When he left she spat out the pills and ground them on the floor with the bottom of her teacup. She then gathered the powder into her hand and blew it out the window, watching it scatter like frightened bugs.

She turned to her sewing machine. At the base, written in English, were the words *Little Betty*. "Hello, Betty," she said. "Where are you from?" From a basket on the floor she picked up a shirt, torn, and placed it on the tray. She couldn't recall to whom it belonged. She cranked the wheel, and the spool on top rotated, unwinding the gray thread. The machine was rusting. Below it, the paint on the desk formed continents.

Through the walls she heard a man's voice on the radio. It was the news. There was to be a UN prisoner exchange with the North and the Chinese. Hill 255 was in the shape of a pork chop, another news segment explained. She wondered who had thought of that first, who called these things such names. Her window faced the front courtyard, and beyond that were the main road and the hills that led to the orphanage. They were in the shape of ears, she thought, the sides of heads. Below her the main entrance opened, and a soldier, discharged, stepped out onto the patio in uniform. He raised his hand to shade his eyes and looked around him as if he wasn't sure where he was and how he had come here.

After Junpei left the orphanage, Miya turned silent. She performed her chores with a mechanical precision and then did more, relieving the other children of their responsibilities. They avoided her, unsure of what to say. She didn't notice. The weeks passed. She slept little, wandering the grounds and out to the field's edge where the forest began.

She was chopping wood behind the kitchen one afternoon when Miss Hara approached her. Together, without speaking, they carried the split logs to the furnaces. She had cut extra and brought them to Miss Hara's cottage, where she placed them at the doorstep. Miss Hara invited her inside. She was a slim woman with a receding hairline. She had long pale fingers that wrapped around her arms as she peered down at Miya.

She had never seen the inside of the house before. It was sparse in its furnishings. A single tea table. A low desk beside the window where the woman kneeled and wrote letters. The walls were unadorned.

Miss Hara owned a single teacup, and that evening they drank tea sitting on the floor, passing the cup back and forth as they watched the fire. Miya expected the woman would mention Junpei in some way, but she didn't. At long last Miss Hara rose and retrieved a sheet of paper and a pencil. "Much to do," she said, and sighed. She told Miya of her plans for the next day. A list was drawn. She handed Miya the list and, smiling, raised her hand and waved her off.

The next day Miya assigned chores to the younger ones: who would be in the garden picking vegetables, milking cows, cooking, washing linen, cleaning the hallways and the dormitory. She made sure the mats were rolled and the floors swept. She enforced curfew. She led the children to the stable and fed the ponies, bringing their manure out to the field, where she spread it over the soil.

She returned to Miss Hara, handing her the list. Miss Hara gave her another one. Again, she drank tea with the woman in silence. Another day came. Another list was given. In the years to come, she would, along with the others her age, begin to tutor the children.

She stayed, as did many. When a new child arrived, she was the first to carry them or take their hand, escorting them into the kitchen. The hours were quick and arduous. In her time, some, like Junpei, ran away, though this was rare. Even so, she grew accustomed to this. And for those who approached her about leaving, Miya and Miss Hara assisted them in obtaining work with the local farmers and the fishermen. They would all gather in front of the orphanage and watch each child depart on a pony, their new employer guiding them down the road. There was even a marriage. They held a wedding ceremony. As a wedding gift the orphans built a house at the end of the field.

All the days ended at Miss Hara's cottage and a single cup of tea. Few words were spoken. Lists were no longer required. Some nights they ignored each other completely, Miss Hara writing her letters, Miya reading a book. At exactly the same hour each day Miss Hara would turn to her and wave her off, flicking her hand.

"Good night, Miss Hara," Miya said, and the woman nodded, smiling.

It was in the summer, in the evening, that she saw the flicker of a lamp at the end of the road. A birthday had been celebrated, marking the day she arrived. She was, by Miss Hara's calculation, twenty-six. Japan was at war. Some of the island's residents had been enlisted to fight alongside them. She sat on the floor, gripping the windowsill, watching the light sway and grow larger. It beat in the rhythm of her heart. When she saw the figure that held it she ran outside.

"Junpei!" she called, running toward him. "Junpei!"

The young man paused, perplexed, and looked at her, raising the lamp to Miya's face. "Aren't you pretty," he said and drank from a bottle of wine. He stepped closer. He ran his fingers down the length of her hair. She didn't move away. He was sweating. "You are not from here," he said. He grasped her hand and lowered it between his legs, and she felt him and stood there, studying the shape of his body.

The broom appeared like a spear thrown across Miya's shoulder. She turned, and there was the shadow of Miss Hara in the dark, raising her arms and beating the man. He had dropped the bottle, and Miss Hara took it, shattered it on the ground, and stabbed the air with the broken bottleneck. She did this until the man was down the road, and when he was gone she turned to Miya, who had begun to cry, and slapped her across the face and continued to do so until Miya fell. Miss Hara left her there.

In the middle of the night, after Miya had returned to the dormitory, Miss Hara came to her and took her back to the house. The woman washed the girl's face. They shared the mat, lying beside each other and looking up at the beams along the ceiling and the starlight that swept over them.

In the first week of August the bombs fell on Hiroshima and Nagasaki. And all the orphans woke one day to find that the Japanese army had left. The Americans came in their place. Cargo trucks could be seen on the roads, and Miya kept waiting for the soldiers to take her and the others away. Instead, supplies were offered to them, including clothing, coffee, sugar, and toys. "Islanders," they were called, with affection, and she realized she had been here for over twenty years.

So the orphanage remained. The school, however, was abandoned. She no longer walked to it. At night she heard the distant engines of trucks and imagined the students leaving and the Americans carrying crates of artwork out of the buildings, sending them off on ships across the Pacific.

Miss Hara had begun to teach her how to sew, from a machine they were given by an American chaplain. They sat beside her desk, and Miya pushed the fabric under the machine's needle while Miss Hara turned the wheel. A lamp was burning, and the shadows of their arms loomed across the floor like birds. By then another war had started, this time on the peninsula.

All of a sudden Miss Hara spoke. "I have my vocation," she said, guiding Miya's fingers. "What will yours be?"

Miya didn't respond. She had never heard Miss Hara speak so many words outside of the classroom. The tapping noise of the sewing machine filled the room, as well as the woman's quick breathing. Her voice remained calm.

"I'm not the judge of this. But there is a world outside of this one. And someday they will go home. And we will be here."

She left to check on their tea. Miya turned the wheel herself. She heard the cup drop and looked back to see Miss Hara's outstretched arm on the floor behind a counter, the cup swiveling rapidly, then slowing. The sewing machine needle punched into Miya's finger.

She would, at times, attempt to recall those hours. It would only come to her in quick images. Her attempts at waking the woman. Running to the barn for a pony. Her own rapid breathing, the tremor of her heart. Her desire to shout, yet inability to. Her inexplicable strength in lifting the body onto the pony's back. Her galloping. Her ascent up the hills and crossing over them. Dusk.

For the second time in her life, she passed through the gates of the school. A young nurse, upon hearing the sound of hooves, stepped out onto the patio. And then, slowly, all the windows filled with the faces of convalescents, their eyes betraying curiosity and bewilderment, this girl on a pony, a woman's body slumped forward against the animal's neck.

The young doctor she would later come to know as Henry stepped forward, carrying a stretcher. The woman was brought inside and placed on a bed. He thought at first she had been wounded. Blood streaked her face and clothes. Henry searched for the source. He couldn't find it. He turned to Miya, and then saw her finger.

She returned to the orphanage after Miss Hara passed away. An American organization had decided to take over the institution. A married couple moved into Miss Hara's cottage. The husband translated. They were from the Midwest, they told Miya, and she didn't know what state that was. Each night they read the Bible before supper. They taught the children English and refused to allow the girls to bathe with the boys. Chaplains visited. Journalists, also. The dormitory filled with orphans from the mainland cities and towns.

Miya lasted there two months. The others stood in front of the orphanage to bid her farewell. She gathered Miss Hara's unsent letters, which she had hidden, her teacup, an extra set of clothes, a comb, and placed them all into a satchel. She carried this and the sewing machine to the car that was to take her back to the hospital.

Later, in the room Henry offered her, she would read over Miss Hara's letters. Most were requesting supplies, from the UN and Christian communities. The last stack, however, was a list: in columns were the names of the orphans, copied onto dozens of sheets of paper in the woman's handwriting, all addressed to refugee camps in the mainland and towns in Japan. *Found,* it stated, at the top.

She looked for herself. She wasn't there, of course. She was nameless when she arrived, her age estimated. As was Junpei. She was about to put the letter away but then paused at the last person on the list. It was written as if it had been an afterthought, the handwriting less confident. She hadn't known Miss Hara's full name until then.

In the washroom down the hall she filled her teacup with water and then added salt taken from the kitchen. It was night, and the washroom was windowless. A light bulb hung from the ceiling, giving off a dull glow. With her hand she covered the cup's opening and shook the liquid mixture. She then rubbed the saltwater onto her teeth and along the base of her gums. What remained in the cup she swooshed in her mouth, and then returned to her room. She didn't bother with the light. Outside the hills faded into sky. She was wearing her hospital gown. She sat on the edge of the bed and combed her hair. The shirt she had sewn lay folded on her desk. Barefoot, she walked downstairs and into the ward.

Two nurses were present, making their rounds. They nodded to her, and she returned their greeting. A weak light shone through the windows, touching the shoulders of the wounded. The sound of a cough. The pulling of sheets. The scent of ether and iodine. She passed the curtain, leaving it parted, and stood above Junpei. She leaned over him, towards the window, and peered out at the tree and the stone garden. The branches swayed. She watched the stones for movement. "Where are you?" she said.

"Where is who?"

She looked down at Junpei. His face was motionless, his eyes still covered. She leaned down and placed her ear against his dry lips.

In the next bed over Benson lifted his arm. He was lying on his back, staring up at the ceiling. His chest was wrapped in gauze. "Where is who?" he repeated.

"Hello, Benson," she said and asked if she could get him anything. He didn't respond.

She crossed the room to the sink and filled a bowl with warm water. She pumped powdered soap into it from the dispenser and then placed it beside Junpei's bed. "You stink," she said, laughing, and patted Junpei's hand. "You've been neglected, you poor thing."

"What did you dream last night?" Benson called.

She didn't know. She unbuttoned Junpei's shirt and spread it out over the ends of the bed. There were bandages speckled across his chest and stomach, covering the sutures. She had watched Henry stitch the wounds, lifting the violet thread and snipping the ends, closing the skin like shells.

"I dreamed of sand," Benson said. "Everywhere. And everyone was sinking into it except me. I walked right over it. Right to the end." He kept his arms raised, swinging them lazily in the air.

She dipped a sponge into the water and worked around Junpei's bandages, scrubbing his body. The soap was perfumed. She hummed to herself, tracing the shape of his arms. She spoke of her day, the blind boy she had recently met. She told him he would have liked the marbles.

"I saw a house once," Benson continued while she washed Junpei's neck. "It had collapsed sideways like a tree. The whole structure. It lay in the middle of an unpaved street. You see. Like this." Benson tilted his arm sideways.

Miya pressed the sponge against Junpei's cheeks, the water running down onto the pillow. She told him of the shirt she had made. For when he woke. She watched Junpei's mouth as Benson's voice hovered over her.

"An older couple lived there," he said. "They had arranged the furniture to accommodate their new floor, which had once been their wall. They refused to leave. The husband was shaking a grenade. His wife remained by the window. She had silver hair. She wore a brooch on her shirt, a flower, a star, I don't remember. I asked to take the wife. The husband refused. I motioned for her. 'Come out the window,' I said. She took my hand and she squeezed my fingers. Her palms were warm. I could smell her insides. And that's the last thing I remember."

Junpei's chest seemed painted under the light of stars, water droplets running along his muscles. It was the nose, she thought, that remained from his boyhood. The flat bridge. His lips, too. The sharp angle of his jaw. She knew them well.

"You moved the stones," she said, rubbing the gauze wrapped over Junpei's forehead. "After the painter finished. You formed the shape of an arrow."

She took Junpei's fingers and placed them between her teeth. She trimmed his nails, which tasted of flour, and swallowed each crescent sliver.

"There," she said. "All better."

A light flashed across the ward then faded. The sound of a car passing the main road. The soft clatter of a nurse's footsteps towards a coughing patient.

"Some nights I dream that house is still there," Benson went on. "It's grown roots. It's sunk. A window is used as a door. The couple's still there, way down below, waving." He turned his head in her direction for the first time. "Doll face," he said. "When you sleep next to that man. I don't know why you do. But you talk in your sleep."

She looked across at Benson. She waited for him to go on. The night had thinned, and the floor of the ward shone. Benson returned to staring at the ceiling. He lifted his hands into moon-light, as if attempting to take hold of it, and then brought them down over his eyes. His lips moved, but what he said she didn't hear. Her vision blurred. She wiped her eyes and looked down at the body she had just washed. "I never left," she said.

Someone touched her shoulder. It was suddenly morning, the light of day abundant. She turned, and her eyes focused on Henry standing behind her. At the foot of the bed was a woman with a receding hairline and long fingers. She wore a long skirt that bil-lowed and a shirt that wrapped across her chest. She was running her hands over Junpei's toes. Miya smiled, thinking this a dream. "You're here," she said, taking Junpei's hand.

Henry remained silent. He was watching her, but she thought little of it. The woman was crying, staring at the body on the bed.

"It's all right," Miya said. "I've kept your sewing machine."

"Miya," Henry said, and took her shoulder again. He leaned forward and spoke into her ear. "Miya. Are you listening?"

She nodded. "It's in my room. Little Betty, it's called."

"Miya. Listen to me."

His voice was steady. She looked to see if Benson was awake, but he wasn't.

"Do I talk in my sleep?" she asked Henry, and he didn't answer. He pointed at Junpei. The blanket was pulled up to his waist and folded back. His shirt lay open, and she apologized, reaching to button it.

Henry took her wrist. He spoke as if from a distance, though she could feel his breath against her cheeks, like wings. "The woman here. This is the boy's mother. She heard about her son and has come to visit him. Do you understand, Miya?"

"Which boy?"

Henry pointed at Junpei. "This one."

"He doesn't have a mother," Miya said. She smiled at him with patience. "Neither of us does. I told you, Henry. Ages ago. Re-member?"

"It's time to stop," Henry said. "It's my fault. I'm sorry, Miya. His mother's here now. She'll be staying with him. You can help the others. Like we agreed." He gripped her arms. "Let's go," he said. "You need to rest."

Miya refused to move from the chair, placing her hands underneath her legs. She turned to the woman. "I kept it. Like you said. I make clothes now." She struggled against Henry's hands, twisting her shoulders. He called her name, a bit louder now, though the more he did so his voice seemed to fade, and she rose, quickly, and leaned over Junpei and held his face. Then she tore away the gauze and lifted his eyelids and saw the emptiness there, a pair of tunnels. The mother began to shout. There were footsteps. She was embraced.

"Junpei," she whispered into where his eyes should have been. "Junpei. I have yet to find it."

She was pulled as if tied to a string, and she fell backwards, her legs giving way. She was caught and dragged across the ward. Her gown skimmed the floor. She watched Henry's body diminish, bending down to pick up her nurse's cap. She saw Junpei's feet, the woman still touching them. The faces of the convalescents passed by her, tall as trees. Out the window the hills swallowed clouds.

Later in the day, Henry visited her room. She had been using the sewing machine, and he sat at the edge of the desk and placed his clipboard beside her. She continued to sew, feeding the fabric through the machine. He lifted her hand and smiled. "It's healed well," he said and let go.

"You have lists," Miya said. "Like Miss Hara."

"That's right," he said. He showed her a piece of paper with her name at the top and a paragraph in his handwriting that he would not let her read. There were dates along the margins as well. *1951* was the first.

"You haven't been taking your medicine," he said.

"I don't have headaches," she said, cranking the wheel.

"Sometimes you have them without realizing, Miya. That's why you should take the medicine. It's for your health that I give them to you. I wouldn't do it if I thought otherwise. Over two years it's been. Since you came. Since we've known each other."

She finished a torn shirt and moved onto a pair of pants.

"You're a great help to us," he said. "You help the wounded. You always have. And always will. I am indebted. But it's getting worse, you see. I think you know that. Each time. Promise me you'll take them."

She listened to footsteps pass them down the corridor. Henry rubbed his face, and she saw his tiredness again.

"There should be paintings," she said. "In the hallways."

"There aren't any," he said. "I've told you this. And there isn't a blind child, either. Now promise to take your medicine."

She hesitated, then agreed.

"Good," he said and handed her a small paper cup. He watched her take them, swallow, and then he leaned down and carelessly sifted through her fabrics. "We wouldn't like it, either," he said. "To be thought of as someone else."

He settled the nurse's cap on her head and tucked a loose strand of her hair behind her ears. He stood to go but paused at the door and watched her. She pretended not to notice. When the American couple had brought her here, she carried the sewing machine under her arm, unwilling to part with it. "A volunteer," Henry had said. "Help is always needed." Together they watched the couple leave by car down the road. "It isn't far," Henry said, and patted her shoulder. "Just across the hills."

One night after the woman came for her son, Miya saw the blind boy. She was in her room, unable to sleep, and heard a strange sound coming from outside the window, not unlike something being dragged across the dirt. She rose and placed her elbows onto the ledge and scanned the lawn, the footpaths, and the gate.

The boy was directly below her. He sat on a bicycle. Its frame seemed to engulf him. The handles were wide, and his arms were outstretched, clinging to the bars. He circled the courtyard, the wheels creating a circle in the dirt, which he followed without error.

"There you are," she said quietly against the windowpane.

She undressed and slipped into the clothes she had worn when she first arrived here, a pair of old pants and a shirt Miss Hara had given her on a birthday. It was imprinted with flowers, and she had said it came from England. Miya took out her satchel from under the bed and placed her comb and Miss Hara's teacup into it. She couldn't find her shoes, so she left barefoot and tip-toed down the corridor and down the stairs. At the ward she paused by the door and heard Benson muttering. Beside him was the comatose patient. And on the chair was the man's mother. Her posture was straight, and she held a book out in front of her, reading under a lamp.

Miya left them and walked down the hallway towards the main entrance. She pushed the door and stepped outside, her body all at once caught by a breeze. The entire courtyard was lit by a heavy moon above the hills. The snow on the fields had melted. It was quiet, save for the gears of the bicycle. She approached the boy, who stopped pedaling and placed his feet on the ground. Tonight, he was wearing a cotton engineer's cap that drooped past his ears.

"Hey, miss," he said. "Want to ride?"

He waved his arm behind him. She raised a leg and sat on the seat. He took his cap off and placed it on her head. "Hold on to my waist," he said. He was thin, and she felt his hipbones push up against her palms. As before, he carried a pouch tied to his belt loop. She lifted her feet. He stood and began to pedal, and the bicycle swayed from their weight. She clutched him. "Miss," he said. "Not so tight." She relaxed. Soon, they were moving down the driveway.

"I pedal," the boy said. "You tell me where we're going."

They reached the end of the hospital property and passed under the gates. "Left," she said, and the boy swerved, and she held him and began to laugh. "Stop!" she called. "Stop."

"You're not very good at this," the boy said, braking.

She got off the bicycle and walked to the fences. She twisted her hair up and hid it underneath the cap, lowering the brim to just above her eyes. A few of the windows of the main hall were lit, and she could distinguish the silhouettes of the nurses walking through the wards. She used to take Junpei here, in those days after they had posed for the painter. She would help him climb the fence, holding his waist. They would shout, "Give us back our faces!" And if anyone approached them, they would run away.

The blind boy tugged on her sleeve. "We go on?"

"We go on."

They continued down the road, following the fences and the hills. The hospital began to shrink from view. Stars gathered along the crests of the distant mountains. They could smell the sea. He pedaled faster. Their bodies pulsed in the darkness. She wondered, as she did sometimes, whether her parents were still underground. A city rebuilt on top of them. It seemed possible.

"Hey, miss," the boy said. "War's ending." He tapped his earlobe. "Listen."

A Profile by Laura van den Berg

Andrea Barrett, after spending years immersed in science and history, recognized her literary calling in a house in western Massachusetts. She was working on a paper about the Franciscans and noticed the narrative threads circulating throughout her research. "I was enrolled in a master's program in Reformation and Medieval History, thinking I might go on to do a Ph.D. and become a historian," Barrett says. Instead, she found herself "making characters and having them exchange dialogue." The impulse to create characters and narratives was "the last brick in the wall. Obviously I wasn't meant to write history. Perhaps I was, then, meant to write stories."

Since then, she has published five novels and two collections, and received the National Book Award and a MacArthur Fellowship. *The Chicago Tribune* has said that "to call Barrett our poet laureate of science is perfectly apropos, as long as we recognize that her specialty is the heart." Despite the accolades, Barrett remains modest about her accomplishments and prefers the solitary life. "I am lucky in having wonderful friends, who are extremely important to me," she says, "but I only seem to understand how to be with people one person at a time. In groups—parties, gatherings, meetings—I am wretchedly uncomfortable and quite awkward." Her uneasiness does not, however, reveal itself in the classroom. From the M.F.A. program at Warren Wilson to Williams College, where she currently works part-time, she has a reputation as a gifted teacher.

She has also remained a relentlessly meticulous writer. Although she takes a meandering, hazy path when embarking on a project, never really having a clear sense of where she's heading, she is a "compulsive re-drafter" who scrutinizes "not only each sentence, but the order of the words in each sentence, the order of the sentences in each paragraph, the order of the paragraphs in each section or scene." She applies the same exactitude to the physical particulars in her fiction, and says her need for precision can complicate her process when she's working with historical material. "If a character is, in 1873, wading into a grotto to look at some sea anemones," she explains, "I can't write the scene until I know exactly *which* sea anemones would have been in that place at that time. And then I also need to know what material the character's skirt was made of so I can understand exactly how heavy and clingy and annoying it would have felt, once it was soaked in the sea. It slows me down a lot." Apart from her historical accuracy, Barrett's work is known for her precise, lyric prose and her vivid evocation of the natural world, whether it be the western Himalayas or Grosse Isle. Nature is not just a backdrop, but serves as a metaphor, catalyst, and an essential companion to the examination of the characters' inner lives.

Born in 1954, Barrett spent her early years in Cape Cod. "I do think growing up on and around the Cape made me alert to the landscape and the living world in ways I might not have been otherwise," she says, adding that "another big influence was simply the fact that we moved very often—every couple of years, usually—always within the same general landscape of the Cape, but shifting schools and sets of friends each time. The constant uprooting meant that I never got to know any one village or school or set of neighbors and schoolmates for very long, which often pained me as a child. But it taught me to turn to other things: to the larger, unchanging aspects of my surroundings." Books became another source of companionship for her. "Characters in books are always with us, and can move around with us. Books really were my most constant friends then, and in some ways they remain so."

Barrett did not complete high school, but left in her junior year—without a diploma—for Union College, where she studied biology, forgoing any courses in literature or creative writing. She graduated in 1974 and briefly attended grad programs in zoology and history. Between leaving college and beginning to publish, she held a variety of jobs: greenhouse worker, receptionist at a box factory, SAT-prep teacher, freelance editor for nursing and medical textbooks, assistant to a dental surgeon, the latter lasting only three days. "None of it was fun," she says. All the while, she read fiction. At first, she only knew about "old books, the 'classics' I could find in small-town bookstores. When I made my first

Barry Goldstein

fumbling attempts to write, in my mid-twenties, I started reading contemporary poetry and literary fiction, and then my world expanded very quickly." She honed her craft for nearly a decade before publishing. "I worked very hard on a novel for about seven years; I had to throw it out, in the end. I spent two years more on another, which I also had to throw out. Finally, humbled—apparently I really was incapable of writing a novel—I tried writing a few stories." She published her first story, "Secret Harmonies," in *The Northwest Review* in 1985, followed by two more in 1987. Soon after, she returned to the novel with her debut, *Lucid Stars,* which appeared in 1988.

Three other novels quickly followed: *Secret Harmonies, The Middle Kingdom,* and *The Forms of Water.* It was, however, a collection of stories, *Ship Fever,* that brought Barrett to real prominence, winning her the National Book Award in 1996. Barrett hadn't focused on stories since her early writing years, but while reading stories and student work for Warren Wilson, her interest in the shorter form was rekindled. "I learned an awful lot. Pacing, economy, structure; how to skip around and over time; how to write lively, scenic summary; how to leave out a great deal and simply suggest," Barrett says. "I learned that as a younger woman, writing my very first stories, I'd made the same mistaken assumption I see many of my students making now: which is that a story, because it is short, must cover only a short amount of time and a compact and tightly defined set of actions. Teaching stories, later on, made me realize that actually the stories I liked best, and wanted to write, were ones that did nearly as much as a novel but in a smaller space."

The stories in *Ship Fever*—as well as in her second collection, *Servants of the Map*—are as expansive as epics, sweeping across generations, cultures, and landscapes. The characters are not content to remain in their houses and yards; they explore, question, and provoke the enigmatic world around them. The stories confront the knotty relationship between humans and the natural world and, in turn, the complexities of the characters' relationships with each other. Historical elements, including appearances by Mendel and Linnaeus, are woven into some of the stories, along with meticulously researched scientific practices: the hybridization of peas, the cataloguing of exotic species, the study of disease, the hibernation patterns of swallows. In Barrett's hands, science comes alive for the reader—never staid or inflexible, but bursting with energy and ambiguity, a source of adventure, discovery, solace, and, for some characters, devastation. While the quantifiable nature of scientific truth often provides a striking contrast to the mysteriousness of human personality, the prospect of meaningful scientific discovery is sometimes just as unreachable as human connection, and the search can bring both rejuvenation and harm.

In one story, "Birds with No Feet," Alec, an animal collector, is wrecked by his desire to conquer nature for personal gains and his competition with a fellow scientist. Throughout the story, everything Alec touches is ruined. During one voyage, a fire breaks out on the ship and his captured animals burn alive. On another excursion, after shooting an orangutan, "his desire for possession carv[ing] a line in the air between his gun and his target," he takes the animal's orphaned offspring back to camp, only to watch him perish from the ague. And later, when Alec finally returns with an impressive collection of animals, America is at war and his achievements go unnoticed, causing him to experience a displacement that plagues nearly all the characters in the collection. It is only after this last blow that Alec realizes he "has never been the scientist he'd believed himself to be, perhaps is no scientist at all." As with all the stories in the collection, the truths of the characters in "Birds with No Feet" represent larger human realities, rendering redemptive qualities alongside fatal flaws.

Voyage of the Narwhal, which followed *Ship Fever* in 1998, was both critically acclaimed and a bestseller. The novel centers around a group of men leaving Philadelphia in 1855 to voyage into the Arctic in search of a lost expedition, and Thomas Mallon described it as "a brilliant reversal of *Heart of Darkness:* the danger is not that the characters will 'go native,' but that a lust for scientific knowledge and intellectual distinction will drive them to cruelties they would have been incapable of before." Barrett's second story collection, *Servants of the Map,* was published four years later, and was a finalist for the Pulitzer Prize. The stories contain links to characters from *Ship Fever* and *Voyage of the Narwhal,* the settings ranging from the early nineteenth century to the twentieth century. While there is a romance to the scientific quests, the adventures and discoveries, the characters are hardly idealized: an obsession with science, in these stories, can fracture marital and familial ties, can lead to disappointment at one's lack of recognition or the ultimate faultiness of their theories. Once again, displacement is a recurring theme, with people longing to leave their mark on the world.

In 2001, Barrett was awarded a MacArthur Fellowship (the "genius grant") and a fellowship at the Center for Scholars and Writers at the New York Public Library. She and her husband moved to New York, that "relentlessly sociable city," for a year, taking up residence in the Williamsburg section of Brooklyn. Barrett, who was doing research for a novel set in a tuberculosis sanatorium, had been in Manhattan for only a few months prior to 9/11. After the attacks, she found herself unable to write. "What was the point? I thought at first," she says in "The Sea of Information," an essay that appeared in *The Kenyon Review* and *The Best American Essays 2005.* As the chaos that followed 9/11 unfolded, she once again sought solace in books and sank deeper into her research, and this textual immersion eventually enabled her to resume writing. "Reading, which gives me access to lives I haven't lived, am not living, probably won't live," she continues in the essay, "is how I find my way to writing: in this case, how I found my way *back* to writing."

While Barrett's preoccupation with science is often foregrounded in her work, the research and historical threads are unfailingly in service of the human story, the search for connection, recognition, and meaning, the sometimes agonizing mysteries of how love can fall short and one's vision of the world can fail. Her aptitude for packing in the wonderful "stuff" of science and history, coupled with exotic locales and physical adventure, distinguishes her work in a crowded field of domestic settings, but what truly makes her fiction remarkable is her ability to traverse the geography of the heart and mind, to bring a sense of order to the wreckage and triumphs of her characters' lives. As she says in "The Sea of Information," "reading and writing are two of the ways we make sense of our mysterious, sometimes terrible world."

In 2004, Barrett accepted a position at Williams College. She and her husband moved into a loft in a mill building in North Adams, where they remain. "I like to walk in the woods with my dog, to snowshoe in winter. In the summer I swim in one of the lakes near us every day the weather permits." She teaches undergraduate writing at Williams College, and, despite the body of work she has amassed, she doesn't take breaks between projects. "I'm always working on something," she says. "If I'm not, you don't want to be around me. If I take a break it's not by choice: either some life emergency has arisen, or I'm sick." After six years, Barrett has completed the novel she began in New York; W.W. Norton will release *The Air We Breathe* this October.

These days, Barrett writes "in a little brick-walled room, sticking out at right angles to the rest of our loft." Long ago, when the loft was part of a functioning mill, her office was a workers' bathroom. "Best," Barrett says with characteristic good humor, "not to think too hard about the symbolism of that."

Laura van den Berg is currently in the M.F.A. program at Emerson College and the editor-in-chief of Redivider. *Her stories have been published or will soon appear in* StoryQuarterly, American Short Fiction, The Literary Review, *and elsewhere.*

Miscellaneous Notes · Fall 2007

COHEN AWARDS Each year, we honor the best poem and short story published in *Ploughshares* with the Cohen Awards, which are wholly sponsored by our longtime patrons Denise and Mel Cohen. Finalists are nominated by staff editors, and the winners—each of whom receives a cash prize of $600—are selected by our advisory editors. The 2007 Cohen Awards for work published in *Ploughshares* in 2006, Volume 32, go to Victoria Chang and Joan Wickersham. (All of the works mentioned here are accessible on our website at www.pshares.org.)

VICTORIA CHANG *for her poem "Proof" in Spring 2006, edited by Kevin Young.*

Victoria Chang was born in Detroit, Michigan, in 1970 and raised in the suburb of West Bloomfield. Her parents were immigrants from Taiwan, her father an engineer at Ford Motor Company and her mother a mathematics teacher in the Detroit school system. Although Chang dabbled in writing as a child, she didn't become serious about it until college. "I started writing because I was conflicted—as a lot of young people can be—about career choices, life in general, gender issues, ethnicity, identity, etc.," she says. At the University of Michigan, she studied Asian history and politics and took a couple of poetry writing workshops on the side. She received an M.A. from Harvard in Asian Studies and then went to work in investment banking and management consulting, later getting an M.B.A. from Stanford. She didn't write any poetry for nearly ten years, but after she left the corporate world to focus on business writing, she returned to get an M.F.A. from Warren Wilson. "My business background has allowed me to be gainfully employed, which is important to me as a woman and as the child of immigrants. Interestingly, not working directly in poetry has allowed me always to have perspective about poetry-related happenings. I don't feel rushed or desperate.

I'm a turtle—I develop slowly and just live my life, work hard at my poems, and hope for the best."

Chang's first book, *Circle,* won the Crab Orchard Review Series in Poetry award, and was published by Southern Illinois University Press in 2005. The book also won the Association of Asian American Studies Book Award. Her poems have appeared in or are forthcoming in *The Paris Review, The Nation, Poetry, The New Republic, The Threepenny Review, The Kenyon Review, The Virginia Quarterly Review, Slate, Pleiades, Ploughshares, TriQuarterly,* and *Best American Poetry 2005.* She is the editor of the anthology *Asian American Poetry: The Next Generation,* published by the University of Illinois Press in 2004. She resides in Irvine, California, and makes her living as a business writer. Currently, she is working on a new manuscript and raising a new baby girl.

About "Proof," Chang writes: "The poem was inspired by little snippets of information from my parents about relatives that I have in Mainland China and what happened to them. My grandmother had left to go to Taiwan during the war, while her sister had stayed in Mainland China, and thus started two entirely different lives that unfolded in very different ways. I often think about how random events like that have led to my being born and my fruitful life in the United States. My great-uncle was killed for being a landowner and an intellectual, like so many people during the Cultural Revolution. Our relatives have contacted us, but I've never met them. Their history and state of poverty is truly overwhelming, and I believe it frightens my parents. For this poem, I thought a straight narrative would be uninteresting, so I wanted to create something different, and thus I used a 'structure,' or the math nomenclature, to help me write the poem."

JOAN WICKERSHAM *for her story "The Woodwork" in Fall 2006, edited by Ron Carlson.*

Joan Wickersham was born in 1957 in New York City and grew up there and in Connecticut. She graduated with a degree in art history from Yale, where she also studied writing with John Hersey. "He emphasized patience, revision, and the need to be steadily and fully dedicated to writing. I wasn't ready for a lot of what he taught, but I remember things he said, and I've understood them better over the years." After college she moved with her husband to the Boston area and worked in advertising. Her first short story appeared in *The Hudson Review* and *The Best American Short Stories* and grew into a novel, *The Paper Anniversary,* published by Viking in 1993. Her work has appeared in publications including *Agni, Glimmer Train, Story,* and *The Boston Globe,* and she has contributed on-air essays to the NPR shows *On Point* and *Morning Edition.* She also writes frequently about architecture, including a regular column, "The Lurker," that she created for *Architecture Boston* magazine.

About "The Woodwork," which concerns suicide, Wickersham writes: "My father committed suicide in 1991. When I got the news, I didn't believe it, but at the same time I thought, 'Of course.' It seemed at once impossible and inevitable; and that was the paradox I started trying to write about. Figuring out how to tell the story took years of false starts. Eventually I completed a numb,  lyrical, chronological, third-person novel which didn't really work, and which I finally set aside. A year later, I was awarded a fellowship at the MacDowell Colony. The first day there, I looked at the draft of the novel, which I had hoped to revise, and saw clearly that what I really needed to do was junk it. Only a couple of pieces survived. Very scary, but necessary. The next day I started writing again, a lot of the same material I'd covered before, but mostly in first-person, and in a way that straddled the line between fiction and memoir. Not in the fudging-the-truth way that has been so controversial in the past few years—I had always been writing about true events that happened around my father's death. The genre questions I struggled with had to do with *how* to tell the story. Create a fictional character and say, 'Her father killed himself'? Or be a little more naked, and say, 'My father killed himself'—but at the same time employ some of the techniques of fiction: dialogue, dramatized scenes, and a less-than-omniscient authorial voice, which seemed particularly important in the case of suicide, where *not* knowing, and never knowing, is such an integral part of the story. The day after I finished another section of the book, I went into the studio expecting to drink tea, listen to music, and putter. But I started thinking about all the people I knew and had met since my father's death who'd had suicide in their families. And about the weird bond that seems to form between people who have experienced this terribly lonely event—how the common experience sort of unites you, but ultimately leaves you alone. Once it got started, 'The Woodwork' poured out in a couple of hours."

Wickersham's book, *The Suicide Index,* will be published by Harcourt next year.

MORE AWARDS Our congratulations to the following writers, whose work has been selected for these anthologies:

BEST STORIES Mary Gordon's "Eleanor's Music," from the Spring 2006 issue edited by Kevin Young, Aryn Kyle's "Allegiance," from the Fall 2006 issue edited by Ron Carlson, and Kate Walbert's "Do Something," from the Winter 2006–07 issue edited by Rosanna Warren, will be included in *The Best American Short Stories 2007*— the most selections from any magazine. The anthology is due out this October from Houghton Mifflin, with Stephen King as the guest editor and Heidi Pitlor as the series editor.

PUSHCARTS Lauren Groff's story "Lucky Chow Fun," from the Fall 2006 issue, and Edward Hirsch's poem "Soustine: A Show of Still Lifes," from the Winter 2005–06 issue edited by David St. John, have been selected for *The Pushcart Prize XXXII: Best of the Small Presses,* which will be published by Bill Henderson's Pushcart Press this November.

DEPARTURES With the production of this issue, Don Lee and David Daniel ended their long time tenure—nineteen and fifteen years respectively—at *Ploughshares.* Don Lee is now teaching creative writing at Macalester College in St. Paul, and David Daniel is the director of undergraduate creative writing at Fairleigh Dickinson University, where he is also a poetry editor for *The Literary Review.* They are indebted to all the staff editors, volunteer readers, interns, and of course guest editors and writers they had the privilege of working with over the years.

*Books Recommended by
Our Staff Editors*

Home Remedies, *stories by Angela Pneuman* (Harcourt): In this dark and spirited debut collection, Pneuman mines the quirks of characters who hail from Kentucky to explore issues of religion, family, death, and sexual attraction. The eight fully realized stories featured here are sharp, well told, and—most important—fearless in their capacity to explore the contradictions both between and within characters. The prose lights up what in other hands might be dreary material: "Prudence figured that a cast-out demon would look like a puddle of split-pea soup the size of a welcome mat, and that it would move around the room, blob-like, trying to absorb its way into people." —*Fred Leebron*

Teeth, *poems by Aracelis Girmay* (Curbstone): The glorious and free-spirited poems of Girmay's first collection move headlong beneath "bejackled" skies, spurred by passions so generous and unhindered as to recall Neruda's magnanimous lyrics. With acrobatic ease, the poet swings from praise to lament, always returning to the heart's motivating ardor for the larger world— its liars, its companions—to champion Love's greater force: "I am sure / my heart was kicking, but there was not / one afternoon I did not climb back up & shove both feet / into the dark Us of your saddle...." —*Cate Marvin*

The Best Place to Be, *a novel in stories by Lesley Dormen* (Simon & Schuster): In this debut fiction, Dormen successfully captures all the pivotal moments in a woman's life—dealing with college, facing the death of her mother, arriving at middle age with grace and humor—although not necessarily in chronological order. "I didn't have any theories," Grace Hanford declares, but she has enough to give this work a real sense of substance while infusing it with funny scenes and mellifluous prose. Here is a character who can feel "some wrong combination of embarrassment and pleasure"; here is a woman who sees men as "the great mystery, the source of all pleasure and pain." Grace Hanford is indeed a "tragedy hound," but her sense of balance between that and human comedy creates a compelling and resonant portrait. —*Fred Leebron*

Sister, *poems by Nickole Brown* (Red Hen): Using umbilicus as guide rail, the speaker of this unflinching and brilliant first book undertakes a hair-lifting expedition back to her childhood, returning to a younger sister both long neglected and longed for. Proving that narrative and lyric are never mutually exclusive, Brown pulls the reader down the channel of her past, which gurgles with the "sound of diesel," to reveal a pedophile—"a man who simply // cannot stop." These poems, always stunning in their clairvoyance, advise us to take such experience and "simply / bury it, but bury it / alive." —*Cate Marvin*

Robert Boswell recommends *House of Bone,* poems by Sheila Black: "This is a complex and surprising collection, a very mature first book of poetry. *House of Bone* is beautifully written, and the poems are genuinely moving. Sheila Black deserves a wide and enthusiastic audience." (Custom Words)

Maxine Kumin recommends *Ultra-Talk,* essays by David Kirby: "Kirby's essays leapfrog from remembering Johnny Cash's 'Folsom Prison Blues' while touring Sicily to a piece called 'Give Me Life Coarse and Rank,' a disquisition on dithyrambs and more in Whitman. My favorite essay, 'Shrouded in a Fiery Mist,' examines the eroticism of Saint Teresa of Avila and Emily Dickinson. In other words, his range is eclectic and smart." (Georgia)

Philip Levine recommends *Space Walk,* poems by Tom Sleigh: "Sleigh's reviewers use words such as 'adept,' 'elegant,' and 'classical.' Reading his new book, I find all those terms beside the point, even though not one is inaccurate. I am struck by the human dramas that are enacted in these poems, the deep encounters that often shatter the participants and occasionally restore them. What delights me most is seeing a poet of his accomplishments and his large and well-earned reputation suddenly veer into a new arena of both our daily and our mythical lives. For the writer, such daring may be its own reward; for the reader, it is thrilling to overhear a writer pushing into greatness." (Houghton Mifflin)

James Alan McPherson recommends *The Interloper,* a novel by Antoine Wilson: "*The Interloper* is an admirable exploration of the complex emotional bond that develops between an imprisoned man and another male, bent on vengeance, who employs the affectations of a female. The exploration of this developing bond will enlighten the novel's readers. Antoine Wilson, a graduate of the Iowa Writers' Workshop, is one of the most talented of emerging writers." (Handsel)

Gerald Stern recommends *My Body,* new and selected poems by Joan Larkin: "Over the decades of writing, Joan Larkin has proved her mastery, whether the poem is mythic, elegiac, or biographical. Her honesty is overwhelming, but it is coupled with poetic cunning, gorgeous language, and a rhythm and tone so precise and appropriate that it is—as in the great poets—transparent. I love reading her poems." (Hanging Loose)

New Books by
Our Advisory Editors

Sherman Alexie, *Flight,* a novel: A troubled teenager is shot back in time, resurfacing as an FBI agent during the civil rights era and an Indian child during the battle of Little Big Horn. Alexie's first novel in ten years is an irrepressible, groundbreaking romp. (Grove)

Ron Carlson, *Five Skies,* a novel: In Carlson's first novel in thirty years, three men gather high in the Rocky Mountains for a construction project and end up revealing themselves in cautiously resonant, profound ways. A voice of striking intimacy and grace. (Viking)

Mark Doty, *Dog Years,* a memoir: In this radiantly unsentimental yet affecting meditation, Doty adopts a second dog as a companion for his dying partner. A moving memoir with reflections on animals and the lessons they teach us. (HarperCollins)

Fanny Howe, *The Lyrics,* poems: With each poem a lament formed in a place of rest, this intense and vital collection responds to Howe's long-term commitment to social justice, weaving through the inconsistencies of the human soul and the inherent violence of humans. (Graywolf)

Maxine Kumin, *Still to Mow,* poems: In her seventeenth book of poetry, Kumin's signature nature poems are luminously invigorated by darker human realities. Potently, she focuses on myriad subjects, including the pleasures of horse keeping, Dick Cheney's "canned hunting," and the disappointments and joys of marriage. (Norton)

Philip Levine, *Tarumba,* translation of poems by Jaime Sabines, with Ernesto Trejo: Sabines is a national treasure in Mexico, and this bilingual edition presents the full power of his secretive, wild, bittersweet poems, stepping into his streets, brothels, hospitals, and cantinas. (Sarabande)

Carl Phillips, *Quiver of Arrows,* selected poems: This generous selection from Phillips's eight books showcases the twenty-year evolution of one of America's most distinctive, original voices, meditating on desire and loss, mastery and subjugation, belief and doubt, sex and human reason. (FSG)

CONTRIBUTORS' NOTES

Fall 2007

KAREN E. BENDER is the author of the novel *Like Normal People* (Houghton Mifflin). Her fiction has appeared in *The New Yorker, Granta, Zoetrope, Plough-shares, The Best American Short Stories,* and *The Pushcart Prize.* She is co-editor of the forthcoming anthology *Choice* (Macadam Cage), and teaches creative writing at the University of North Carolina at Wilmington.

JILL GILBRETH received her M.F.A. from Emerson College. She lives in North Adams, Massachusetts, and teaches literature and writing at Massachusetts College of Liberal Arts. This is her first publication.

BRET ANTHONY JOHNSTON is the author of *Corpus Christi: Stories.* In 2006, he received a National Book Award honor for writers under thirty-five. He is Director of Creative Writing at Harvard, and may be reached at bretanthonyjohnston.com.

ELLEN LITMAN was born in Moscow, Russia, where she lived until 1992. Her fiction has appeared in *Best New American Voices 2007, Best of Tin House, TriQuarterly, The Ontario Review,* and elsewhere. Her novel in stories, *The Last Chicken in America,* will be published by W.W. Norton in the fall of 2007.

MARGARET MCMULLAN has written four novels, including *When I Crossed No-Bob* and *In My Mother's House.* Her work has appeared in *Glamour, The Chicago Tribune, Southern Accents, TriQuarterly, Michigan Quarterly Review, The Greensboro Review, Other Voices,* and *Boulevard.* She is currently a professor of English at the University of Evansville in Evansville, Indiana.

LISA NILSSON grew up in Avon, Massachusetts, where she found early inspiration in family members who painted houses and watercolors, repaired car bodies, and mixed colors for false teeth. In 2003 she moved with her husband, Rich Remsberg, to North Adams. Other work can be seen at Mass MoCA, in the show "Boxed Sets: Assembling Objects, Images, and People."

ALIX OHLIN is the author of *The Missing Person* (2005) and *Babylon and Other Stories* (2006). Her stories have appeared in *Best New American Voices, The Best American Short Stories,* and on NPR's "Selected Shorts." She teaches at Lafayette College in Easton, Pennsylvania.

PETER ORNER was born in Chicago and is the author of the collection *Esther Stories* and the novel *The Second Coming of Mavala Shikongo,* winner of the Bard Fiction Prize and finalist for the *Los Angeles Times* Book Prize. In 2006, Orner was awarded a fellowship from the Guggenheim Foundation.

KAREN SHEPARD is the author of three novels, *An Empire of Women, The Bad Boy's Wife,* and, most recently, *Don't I Know You?* She teaches writing and literature at Williams College in Williamstown, Massachusetts, where she lives with her husband, the novelist Jim Shepard, and their three children.

JOAN SILBER is the author of *Ideas of Heaven: A Ring of Stories,* a finalist for the National Book Award and for the Story Prize. A new novel will be published by W.W. Norton in spring 2008. She lives in New York and teaches at Sarah Lawrence College.

SARAH STONE is the author of *The True Sources of the Nile* and co-author, with Ron Nyren, of *The Longman Guide to Intermediate and Advanced Fiction Writing* (also published in a textbook version as *Deepening Fiction: A Practical Guide for Intermediate and Advanced Fiction Writers*). She teaches in the M.F.A. program at New College of California and at San Francisco State University.

CHRISTOPHER TILGHMAN is the author of the novels *Mason's Retreat* and *Roads of the Heart,* and the story collections *The Way People Run* and *In a Father's Place.* He teaches at the University of Virginia.

PAUL YOON's work has appeared or is forthcoming in *One Story, Post Road, Salamander, Glimmer Train, TriQuarterly, American Short Fiction,* and elsewhere. He was included in *The Best American Short Stories 2006,* edited by Ann Patchett, and was recently selected as an emerging writer for PEN/New England's Discovery Night.

~

GUEST EDITOR POLICY *Ploughshares* is published three times a year: mixed issues of poetry and fiction in the Spring and Winter and a fiction issue in the Fall, with each guest-edited by a different writer of prominence, usually one whose early work was published in the journal. Guest editors are invited to solicit up to half of their issues, with the other half selected from unsolicited manuscripts screened for them by staff editors. This guest editor policy is designed to introduce readers to different literary circles and tastes, and to offer a fuller representation of the range and diversity of contemporary letters than would be possible with a single editorship. Yet, at the same time, we expect every issue to reflect our overall standards of literary excellence. We liken *Ploughshares* to a theater company: each issue might have a different guest editor and different writers—just as a play will have a different director, playwright, and cast—but subscribers can count on a governing aesthetic, a consistency in literary values and quality, that is uniquely our own.

~

SUBMISSION POLICIES We welcome unsolicited manuscripts from August 1 to March 31 (postmark dates). All submissions sent from April to July are returned unread. In the past, guest editors often announced specific themes for issues, but we have revised our editorial policies and no longer restrict submissions to thematic topics. Submit your work at any time during our reading period; if a manuscript is not timely for one issue, it will be considered for another. We do not recommend trying to target specific guest editors. Our backlog is unpredictable, and staff editors ultimately have the responsibility of determining for which editor a work is most appropriate.

Mail one prose piece or one to three poems. We do not accept e-mail submissions, but we now accept submissions online. Please see our website (www.pshares.org) for more information and specific guidelines. Poems should be individually typed either single- or double-spaced on one side of the page. Prose should be typed double-spaced on one side and be no longer than thirty pages. Although we look primarily for short stories, we occasionally publish personal essays/memoirs. Novel excerpts are acceptable if self-contained. Unsolicited book reviews and criticism are not considered.

Please send only one manuscript at a time, either by mail or online. Do not send a second submission until you have heard about the first. *There is a limit of two total submissions per reading period, regardless of genre, whether it is by mail or online.* Additional submissions will be returned unread. Mail your manuscript in a page-size manila envelope, your full name and address written on the outside. In general, address submissions to the "Fiction Editor," "Poetry Editor," or "Nonfiction Editor," not to the guest or staff editors by name, unless you have a legitimate association with them or have been previously published in the magazine. Unsolicited work sent directly to a guest editor's home or office will be ignored and discarded; guest editors are formally instructed not to read such work. *All mailed manuscripts and correspondence regarding submissions should be accompanied by a business-size, self-addressed, stamped envelope (S.A.S.E.) for a response only. Manuscript copies will be recycled, not returned.* No replies will be given by postcard or e-mail (exceptions are made for international submissions).

Expect three to five months for a decision. We now receive well over a thousand manuscripts a month. Do not query us until five months have passed, and if you do, please write to us, including an S.A.S.E. and indicating the postmark date of submission, instead of calling or e-mailing. Simultaneous submissions are amenable as long as they are indicated as such and we are notified immediately upon acceptance elsewhere. We cannot accommodate revisions, changes of return address, or forgotten S.A.S.E.'s after the fact. We do not reprint previously published work. Translations are welcome if permission has been granted. We cannot be responsible for delay, loss, or damage. Payment is upon publication: $25/printed page, $50 minimum and $250 maximum per author, with two copies of the issue and a one-year subscription.

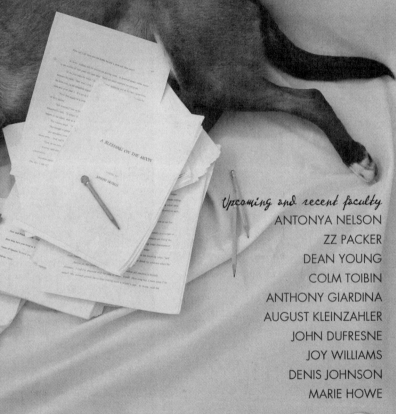

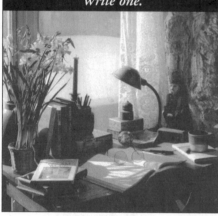

Our graduates don't just write.
They publish.

MASTER OF FINE ARTS IN
Creative Writing
Concentrations in Fiction, Poetry, and Nonfiction

MASTER OF ARTS IN
Publishing & Writing
Concentrations in Book, Magazine,
and Electronic Publishing

Emerson College offers a thriving community of writers with diverse backgrounds and interests, as well as students aspiring to work in the publishing industry. Defined by close collaboration and support from faculty and fellow students, our Creative Writing and Publishing & Writing programs connect Emerson students to Boston's distinguished literary tradition. Immerse yourself in the writing life at Emerson College, home of the renowned journal *Ploughshares*.

EMERSON COLLEGE
BOSTON MASSACHUSETTS

Emerson College
Office of Graduate Admission
120 Boylston Street
Boston, MA 02116

www.emerson.edu
gradapp@emerson.edu
617-824-8610

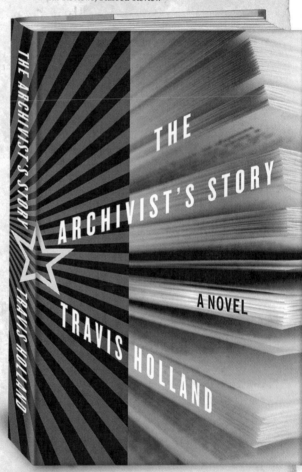

THE BOSTON UNIVERSITY
M.F.A. IN CREATIVE WRITING

Our program, one of the oldest and most prestigious in the nation, is small (our workshops are limited to the ten students admitted in any genre); very intensive (the M.F.A. is usually awarded after one year and must be completed in two); and highly competitive (normally twenty-five students apply for each spot in fiction and poetry). We are best known for the quality of our graduate workshops. All of these are held in the same small room, which allows through its dusty windows a glimpse of the Charles River. Perhaps the most remarkable such workshop occurred when Sylvia Plath, Anne Sexton, and George Starbuck gathered for instruction by Robert Lowell—gathered, by the way, less often in that little room than at the Ritz Bar. These days, the poetry workshops are run by Robert Pinsky, Rosanna Warren, and Derek Walcott, who also conducts playwriting workshops; and those in fiction are led by Leslie Epstein and Ha Jin. Because our students have about them the resources of a great university they might also find themselves in classes taught by such superb scholars as Elie Wiesel and Christopher Ricks.

It is difficult to know how best to measure a student's success, or the worth of a program to a writer; we can say that our graduates in each genre have accomplished a good deal. Among numerous awards, our playwrights can list the Heideman Award, two Elliot Norton Awards, three National Playwriting Awards from the Kennedy Center, six IRNE Awards, commissions from The Huntington Theatre Company, Laguna Playhouse, The Kennedy Center, South Coast Repertory, and Steppenwolf Theatre. Our graduates in poetry have won the $30,000 Whiting Award, the Barnard New Women Poets Series, a grant from the NEA, and the Norma Farber First Book Award; there have been three winners in three years of the Discovery/The Nation Award, and two winners of the National Poetry Series. In fiction, our students have also won the Whiting Award, and a few years ago, our writers swept every major literary award in the country, with Ha Jin winning the National Book Award and the PEN/Faulkner, and Jhumpa Lahiri the PEN/Hemingway and the Pulitzer Prize. Every few months a graduate of our program brings out a book with a major publisher; and some, like Sue Miller and Arthur Golden, spend a good deal of time on best-seller lists. Over the last decade we have placed more than a score of our graduates in tenure-track positions at major American universities (Peter Ho Davies and Carl Phillips direct the programs at Michigan and Washington University in St. Louis). We make, of course, no such assurances. Our only promise to those who join us is of a fair amount of time in that river-view room, time shared with other writers in a common, most difficult pursuit: the perfection of one's craft. For more information about the program, visiting writers, and financial aid (our teaching fellows conduct undergraduate creative writing classes and may teach at the Boston Arts Academy, a pilot high school), write to Director, Creative Writing Program, Boston University, 236 Bay State Road, Boston, MA 02215 or visit our website at *www.bu.edu/writing/*.

Application deadline is March 1, 2008.

Boston University is an equal opportunity, affirmative action institution.

BOSTON REVIEW

ANNOUNCES ITS FIFTEENTH ANNUAL
FICTION CONTEST

judge
CHRIS ABANI

first prize
$1,500

deadline
OCTOBER 1, 2007

PARTIAL RULES Stories should not exceed 4,000 words and must be previously unpublished. Manuscripts should be submitted with a cover note listing the author's name, address, and phone number; names should not appear on the stories themselves. Simultaneous submissions are not eligible. A $20 entry fee ($30 for international submissions), payable to BOSTON REVIEW in the form of a check or money order, must accompany each story entered. Entrants will receive a one-year subscription to BOSTON REVIEW. Manuscripts will not be returned. Send entries to Fiction Contest, Boston Review, 35 Medford St., Suite 302, Somerville, MA 02143
COMPLETE RULES ONLINE AT BOSTONREVIEW.NET